10.⁰⁰

o,p

PENNSYLVANIA CLOCKS
AND CLOCKMAKERS

Governments, like Clocks, go from the motion
Men give them: and as Governments are made and
mov'd by Men, so by them they are Ruin'd too:
  Wherefore
Governments rather depend upon Men, than Men
upon Governments.
Let Men be good, and the Government can't be bad;
if it be ill, they will cure it; But if Men be bad
let the Government be never so good, they will
endeavor to warp and spoil it to their Turn.
WILLIAM PENN

Preface to the Frame of Government for
Pennsylvania. 1682.

PENNSYLVANIA
CLOCKS
AND CLOCKMAKERS

An Epic of Early American Science,

Industry, and Craftsmanship

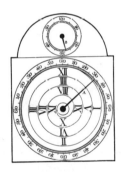

by George H. Eckhardt

Illustrated

BONANZA BOOKS

This Book is Dedicated to

BENJAMIN TYSON SCHMAUK

1853 – 1939

GENTLEMAN AND CLOCKMAKER
WHO CARRIED FORWARD THE TRADITIONS OF
THE PAST AND PRESERVED THEM
FOR THE FUTURE

FOREWORD

THE clocks of early Pennsylvania stand as monuments to a people of a great Commonwealth. Being unique, these clocks are widely sought after by collectors today. And to the collectors it might be well to give some thought; for they have played an important part in presenting the history of America. By saving from oblivion the things of the past, they arouse interest in the people who lived with these things. And this is singularly true of the tall case clocks of Pennsylvania.

This book has been written to furnish information about these clocks and their makers. It is the first book devoted to the subject. When information is desired about the clocks of Pennsylvania, it has been necessary to search through monographs, articles and records not readily accessible. Writers have hitherto confined themselves to individual counties of Pennsylvania or to individual clockmakers. The several excellent books on American clocks have little to say about the timepieces of Pennsylvania.

Today, Pennsylvania clocks may be found distributed throughout the nation—and abroad, where they have been carried by the descendants of the original owners. They are few in number compared to New England clocks, yet one can always be found with a little searching. Frequently they appear in sales and in the hands of dealers, but for the most part they are cherished heirlooms.

The Pennsylvania clockmaker usually dealt with the original owner on a personal basis. At least the two were known to each other, and there was a deep sense of responsibility in this relationship. The New England clocks now generally met with, however, especially those of the first half of the nineteenth century, were made in keen trade competition—the work of men who never met the people who bought the clocks.

Practically all Pennsylvania clocks were of the weight-and-pendulum type in a tall case—now know as the "grandfather's clock." The name can be traced to Philadelphia; it was originated by a songwriter who successfully portrayed the deep feelings of a people toward their clocks.

For more than a century and a half, from 1682 to 1850, there were few, if any, innovations in basic design, yet each Pennsylvania clock was an individual creation, and it may be said that no two are exactly alike.

Colonial cabinet makers often lavished their best craftsmanship on clock cases. Some of these, in Pennsylvania, represent the finest examples of cabinet work of their respective periods.

This book has been planned to furnish the student, owner, and prospective owner of Pennsylvania clocks with information necessary to appreciate and enjoy these timepieces. It is sincerely hoped that the book will direct attention to those clocks and their makers and inspire further research into this fascinating subject. As far as possible we shall permit the clocks to tell their own stories.

The first part of the book gives information about the weight-and-pendulum clock in a tall case and its importance in Pennsylvania. It was in this Commonwealth that scientists, pioneers in the building of steamboats and railroads, as well as patriots, came from the ranks of clockmakers.

Highly technical details have been avoided but not at the sacrifice

of accuracy. Several matters about which not many people are familiar—such as the "almanac built into the clock," the moon wheel—
are explained.

The care, repair, restoration, and appraising of these clocks are
discussed so that the owners and prospective owners may rely upon
their own knowledge and judgment.

While the clockmaker was, for the most part, also a watchmaker some early Philadelphians devoted their energies exclusively
to watches. The American watch factory did not come into full being
until about 1850; before this, watches either were the work of individuals or were imported. The importation of watch works brought
about the craft of watch case maker.

It is of great significance that clocks at the present time are passing
another milestone in their history: three centuries ago, in 1656, timekeeping passed into an era of scientific accuracy when Christiaan Huygens applied the pendulum. Today, timekeeping is turning to elec-
tronics, and the quartz crystal is taking the place of the pendulum as
the controlling element in clocks designed as standard timepieces for
observatories.

The *Horologium* of Huygens, in which he first described his
clock, has finally been translated from the original Latin into English.
It is the first detailed description of a pendulum-controlled clock and
still one of the best. For this reason and because Pennsylvania and the
weight-and-pendulum clock grew up together, as it were, the translation is included in this book.

While the interest in timekeeping and clocks is spreading widely,
it is surprising how few have a grasp of the fundamentals involved.
These are not difficult to understand, and a knowledge of them adds
greatly to one's appreciation of clocks; for this reason the present book
makes available the first English account of what William Molyneux
so aptly called "the business of time." Molyneux was the precursor of
Thomas Jefferson and, more than any other man, set the pattern for
those patriot-scientists who were so intensely interested in clocks and
timekeeping.

The second part of the book is made up of portraits of Pennsylvania clocks arranged in chronological order. This section may be

used to study and date specimens by comparison. As far as possible, portraits of clocks are presented that have not appeared in other books. An effort has also been made to present clocks now in museums or public collections, so that those who wish to study them further may find them.

The third part of the book is made up of an authentic and annotated list of the clock- and watchmakers of Philadelphia and Pennsylvania from 1682 until 1850. Few clocks or watches now of interest to collectors were made in Pennsylvania after 1850, and these few exceptions have been included.

This list had its origin more than half a century ago when B. T. Schmauk, a clockmaker of Philadelphia, began listing all clocks that passed through his hands. After his death the list was turned over to the writer and the present list was built upon it as a foundation. The original list has been corrected, added to, and revised over a period of years.

Careful consideration was given to the question of whether or not a bibliography should be included in this book. A comprehensive and worthwhile bibliography of the books on time, clocks and watches —or even a list of the books, pamphlets and articles consulted in the preparation of this book—would be a book in itself. It also must be realized that there already exist several rather complete bibliographies on the subject of horology. For these reasons it was decided not to include a bibliography.

The author suggests that those interested in the various phases of the art and science of horology consult *Bibliographie Générale de la Mesure du Temps* published by Tardy, Paris. The work is not dated but it appeared about 1943. It is available and can be found in most large libraries. This is a fairly comprehensive list of all works published on the subject in English, French, German, etc. One need not fear the barrier of languages, since each work is outlined in the language in which it was published. There is a subject index.

GEORGE H. ECKHARDT

Philadelphia
June 1955

ACKNOWLEDGMENTS

IT would be presumptuous indeed for the author to claim complete originality for this book; the better the book the more the author had to search through the works of those who have gone before him. And it would be impossible to list the names of the many people who have generously shared information and otherwise aided in this work. To all these the author expresses his appreciation.

Throughout the book, credit is given to individuals and institutions at home and abroad, who have supplied specific information. This credit is small reward for their kindnesses.

Credit must, however, be expressed to the Rev. John E. Bresnahan, O.S.A., of Villanova University, for his translation of the *Horologium* and to the Rev. Daniel P. Falvey, O.S.A., librarian of that institution; to Mr. Humphry M. Smith, of the Royal Greenwich Observatory; to the Council of the Royal Society; to the American Philosophical Society, and The Franklin Institute.

The author here also expresses his gratitude to certain individuals without whose help and encouragement the book would never have been completed. Among these are the late Charles Messer Stow, of the old New York *Sun*, and the late Homer Eaton Keyes, of the magazine *Antiques*, who helped lay the foundations; and Messrs. Robert A. Franks and Penrose R. Hoopes, who helped to build on those foundations.

Appreciation is also expressed to the staff of the Rijksmuseum voor de Geschiedenis der Natuurwetenschappen (National Museum of the History of Science), The Netherlands, for helpful cooperation in preparing the chapter on Huygens and his works.

The works of Huygens have been published in a monumental modern edition, "Oeuvres complètes de Christiaan Huygens, publiées par la Société hollandaise des sciences, chez Martinus Nijhoff, La Haye." Volume I bears the date 1888 and the last volume (XXII) is in the press. This edition contains all Huygens's printed works, his correspondence, and hitherto unpublished material from manuscripts in the Leiden University Library. Volumes XVII and XVIII contain his researches in horology. The books are available in larger libraries in the United States.

CONTENTS

ILLUSTRATIONS

PENNSYLVANIA CLOCKS
AND CLOCKMAKERS

1

THE PENNSYLVANIA CLOCK

The weight-and-pendulum clock in a tall case, now universally known as the grandfather's clock, and the Commonwealth of Pennsylvania came into being in the same period. This cannot be dismissed as a mere coincidence.

In the latter part of the seventeenth century, and on into the eighteenth, men were seeking the true principles of science, government, and life itself. There was a great ferment of thought, and this brought about action. Pennsylvania and the weight-and-pendulum clock were both products of this action, and the clocks and their makers became enmeshed in the life and history of the Commonwealth.

In this environment of liberating ideas, William Penn, himself a member of the Royal Society, founded Pennsylvania in 1682, a colony "which should open its doors to every kindred, tongue and nation: which should transplant from the Old World the best in arts, sciences and culture: which should minimize human weakness by a full exercise of the Christian Gospel, including the benighted Indian, within its beneficent light."

The weight-and-pendulum clock in a tall case was becoming known in England by the time Pennsylvania was founded. This type of clock had its start when Christiaan Huygens, a Dutch scientist of note, applied the pendulum as the controlling element of a timepiece. Huygens stated that he made his invention late in 1656 and that it was available to the people "of his own country" a few months later. He described it in a small book published in 1658.

The application of the pendulum to clocks revolutionized clockmaking and brought to timekeeping an accuracy hitherto impossible. Huygens's invention was largely inspired by his need for an accurate timekeeper to be used in making astronomical observations. In 1673 he published his great work on the clock and pendulum in which he fully described and explained the theory of the latter.

Huygens worked with a comparatively short pendulum, and the construction of his clock was such that the pendulum required a very wide arc through which to swing.

The invention of the anchor escapement in the 1670s, whereby the "seconds" pendulum—thirty-nine inches long and vibrating through a small arc—could be employed, cleared the path for making the weight-and-pendulum clock in a tall case practical.

This invention—one of the great achievements in horology—is usually attributed to Robert Hooke, the English experimental philosopher, and the date is given as 1676. However, there is evidence that the anchor escapement was really invented by William Clement in 1671. Hooke was a very active man in an age of great scientific discovery, and his investigations were "so prolific that there was scarcely a discovery made in his time which he did not conceive himself entitled to claim."

The anchor escapement—together with an improvement, the dead beat escapement invented by George Graham in 1715—brought about a basic design for clocks which was so efficient that men could do little to improve upon it during the succeeding two centuries or more. This excellent basic design was accepted by the clockmakers of Pennsylvania and perfection was sought in honest workmanship rather than in innovations.

Today we cannot be certain whether or not the tall case for a

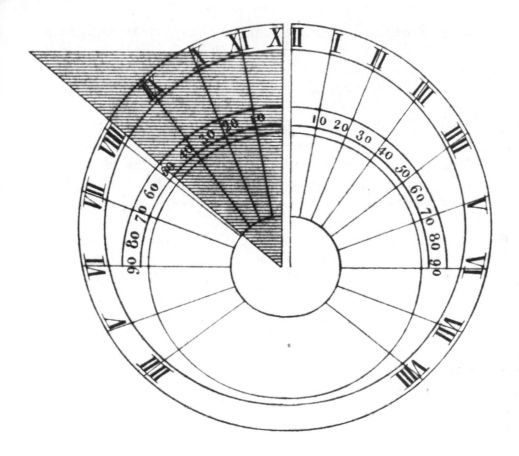

The sun dial is a dial upon which a shadow indicates solar or sun time. The object casting the shadow is known as the rod, style, or gnomon. To be accurate throughout the year, a sun dial must be designed and constructed for the latitude of the place where it is to be used. (Latitude is the distance on the earth's surface north or south of the equator, measured in degrees.)

Dialing—the design and construction of sun dials—involves astronomy, geography, geometry, and mathematics, as well as art and architecture. During the 16th and 17th centuries many books were written on the subject. The sun dial may take many forms—horizontal, vertical, or inclined—according to the position of the plane of the dial with respect to the horizon. At its best, the sun dial never measured time, it merely indicated it.

clock was an English or Dutch invention. The Dutch were partial to wall clocks. The fact remains that the tall clock case was a happy thought no matter who invented it. The clock now became an important and decorative piece of furniture in addition to being a timekeeper. The dial was on a level with the eyes and the clock could be wound and adjusted easily. The weights were concealed and the entire mechanism was protected from dust.

The tall case offered so many advantages that a few clocks with the short pendulums of Huygens were housed in tall cases even before the invention of the anchor escapement made the use of the long "seconds" pendulum possible.

To appreciate what was happening in the world of science while Pennsylvania was in its first decade of existence, it is only necessary to recall that in 1687 Sir Isaac Newton published his *Philosophiae Naturalis Principia Mathematica*. He welded together the work of scientists who had preceded him, demonstrated the fundamental laws of motion, mass, force and acceleration, and presented the laws of gravitation—"the greatest scientific generalization of the human mind at that time, if not for all time."

On William Penn's second visit to Pennsylvania in 1699 he brought with him, as his secretary, James Logan, a scholar and lover of books who was familiar with the works of Newton and other scientists. Largely through Logan the seeds of learning were planted and nourished in Pennsylvania and the stage set for the entrance of Benjamin Franklin, through whose efforts Philadelphia became the "Athens of America."

In an era of scientific progress, the measurement of time took on a new importance. Opportunities were opening to greater numbers in trade and commerce, and time became an increasingly important factor in the lives of people. Clocks ceased to be luxuries, they became a necessity.

It may be well to review briefly the history of timekeeping before the advent of the weight-and-pendulum clock. Time has been likened to a mighty river whose unvarying stream passes before man. The problem has been to measure the flow of this river of time and record it.

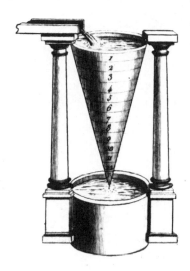

The clepsydra or water clock was a device for measuring time by the controlled passage of water. The word "clepsydra" is derived from two Greek words meaning thief of water. Going back to the second century B.C., or even earlier, the water clock in its most simple form consisted of a vessel with a small hole in its base. When filled to a certain mark, this vessel would empty itself in approximately the same intervals of time. Another simple form consisted of an arrangement whereby water trickled into a vessel at a uniform rate. The receiving vessel had marks on its wall indicating the various hours.

The earth's rotation on its axis each day is uniform. Accordingly, from the very first, the earth has been man's basic timekeeper and in it we have had an unvarying standard.

The sun dial, going back to biblical days, was probably man's first effort to "tell" time. In the early days of his history, man did not know that the earth rotated upon its axis but he did observe the sun's apparent path across the heavens and the fact that it cast different shadows at different times of the day. But the sun dial at its best did not *measure* time—it merely *indicated* it.

To measure time, the clepsydra, or water clock, was invented about the second century, B.C. This was essentially a vessel with a small opening in its base through which water flowed at a uniform rate. This rate of flow was calibrated against the passage of time. As water slowly flowed from the vessel, time could be measured, since there was a direct relationship between the height of water remaining in the vessel and the time elapsed or "run out."

The sand glass worked on the same principle, using sand instead of water. When the vessel of the water clock was empty, it could be refilled; when the sand ran out, the glass could be reversed. Some water clocks became very elaborate and complicated, and a certain degree of accuracy was achieved.

Today we are not certain who made the first mechanical clock—a device of wheels driven by weights. In 996 A.D., Gerbert, a Benedictine monk, who later became Pope Sylvester II, made a clock for the cathedral at Magdeburg. This may have been the first mechanical clock or it may have been a very elaborate water clock. The confusion in the record arises from the fact that scholars, writing in Latin, used the word *horologium* for all types of clock.

Let us consider the difference in principle between the water clock and the mechanical clock. The water clock attempted to measure time by comparing the regulated and known flow of water in the clock with the passage of time. It was a flowing process, continuous as long as water was supplied to the clock.

But it was not until the clock was given a periodic or intermittent motion that any great degree of accuracy could be expected. It is obvious that the proper way to measure anything, including time, is to measure by means of small, equal and separate units or intervals. We are all familiar with the ticking of the mechanical clock, which is the audible manifestation of what the device is actually doing—ticking off time.

The first mechanical clock of which we have definite record and knowledge was made by Henry De Vick in the late 1300s, or thereabouts, for Charles V of France. A description of this clock is extant, but unfortunately it was not written until some three and a half centuries after the clock was made, and we do not know what changes might have been made in that long interval.

We can be certain, however, that by the end of the fourteenth century the mechanical clock had arrived at a basic form which persisted for almost three centuries until the invention of the pendulum

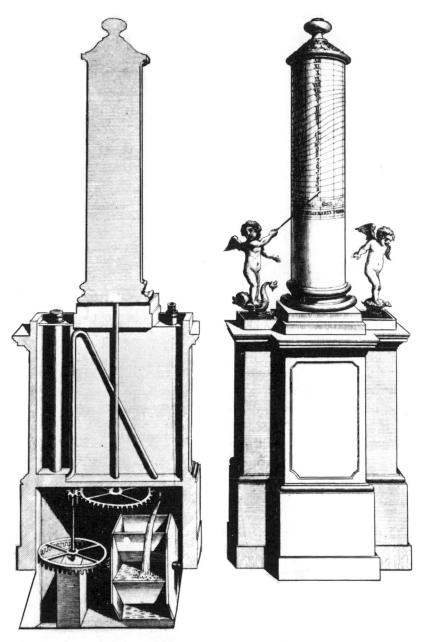

From simple beginnings, water clocks developed into elaborate designs with mechanical features but always relying upon the controlled passage of water as the basic principle. Water clocks were extensively used up until the Middle Ages. The water clock actually attempted to measure time rather than merely indicate it.

clock. This earlier clock was weight driven; the controlling element consisted of a crown wheel, verge, and foliot balance.

All are familiar with the oft-told story of how Galileo observed the swaying of the chandelier suspended by a long chain from the ceiling of the church in Pisa. Using his own pulse to time the vibrations, he discovered that the period, or time, of each vibration seemed the same regardless of the length of arc through which the chandelier swung.

It was Christiaan Huygens who put the observations of Galileo to practical use when he applied the pendulum as the controlling element of a clock. Ahasuerus Fromanteel, a Dutch clockmaker and friend of Huygens, is credited with having introduced the pendulum clock in England.

Opposite. The mechanical clock, late 14th century to 1656. By the late 14th century the mechanical clock was established, and its form consisted essentially of a train of weight-driven wheels, the controlling element of which was a heavy bar—known as the foliot balance—swinging to and fro. This basic form of control, with slight variations, persisted for almost three centuries until superseded by the pendulum. It was also applied to spring-driven clocks. Included in this mechanism was an upright rod, known as the verge, which was suspended from a support by means of a cord. This rod turned in suitable holes in the frame, which holes served as guides. The verge carried a heavy horizontal bar—the foliot balance—fixed near its top to form a letter T. There were notches on the upper side of the bar so that two weights could be adjusted at various distances from the center, giving a rough adjustment of the bar's period of swing: the farther the weights were placed from the center the slower the swings of the bar.

The verge was also fitted with two small plates known as pallets, so arranged that they alternately engaged the upper and lower teeth of the crown wheel; this was a circular band attached to the end of an arbor or axle. Teeth were cut in the outer rim of this band so that it resembled a crown, hence the name.

The paramount difficulty of this system was that the foliot balance had no fixed period of oscillation, hence a clock so controlled could only approximate accuracy.

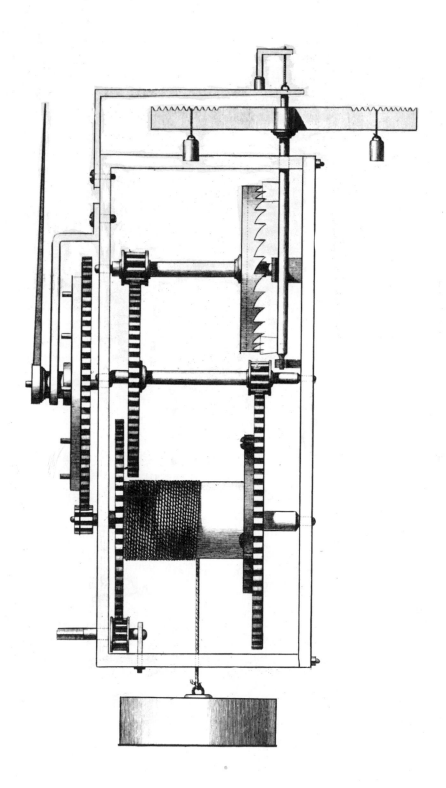

As is usual with great scientific discoveries, there is some confusion regarding other men who worked with the pendulum at an early date, but the foregoing facts are sufficient for our purpose.

Dates are particularly important in studying the clocks of Pennsylvania, since claims often arise which cannot be substantiated, simply because they are contrary to the milestones in the history of Pennsylvania and clocks. The brief comparative chronology on pages 14 and 15 will be sufficient to help avoid such errors in the years marking the beginning of both the weight-and-pendulum clock in a tall case, and the history of Pennsylvania.

In 1683, one year after its founding, Philadelphia had a population of five hundred and there were eighty dwelling houses. William Carter was then working as a watchmaker and repairer. David Vaughan is mentioned as a watchmaker in 1695.

Gabriel Thomas visited Pennsylvania in 1697 and a year later published his *An Historical and Geographical Account of the Province and Country of Pennsilvania*. He reported that there were then "above two thousand noble houses" in Philadelphia and that craftsmen, including watchmakers and clockmakers, earned from two to three times as much in Philadelphia as in London for similar work.

However, Philadelphia was at first a small town compared to Boston. A view of the city painted about 1720 by Peter Cooper shows a conglomeration of red brick houses with hardly a steeple or tower above them.

In the manuscript minutes of the Common Council of Philadelphia, now preserved in the Free Library of that city, may be found the following notation under date of February 26, 1717: "Peter Stretch Exhibited an Account of Work done, and several Disbursements on the Towne Clock, w[hi]ch was read and the Sum of Eight Pounds, Eighteen shillings and ten pence allowed him."

Many have taken this to mean that Philadelphia had a public tower clock at this early date. As a matter of fact the city did not have a truly public clock until more than three decades later; the first public clock of which there is an authentic record was the one ordered for the State House in 1752. The construction of the State House was not begun until 1732.

Gabriel Thomas, late in the seventeenth century, wrote that Philadelphia had a "stately Towne House or Guild Hall," and this would seem to refer to the Court House, although others believe that this building was not erected until a few years later. In any event the city did have a court house about 1710, in which the municipal government and courts met. The Assembly of Pennsylvania had no fixed meeting place until the State House was built.

The Common Council of Philadelphia, of which Peter Stretch was a member, met in the Court House. This building never had a public tower clock. Therefore it would seem that the clock for which Peter Stretch received money for "work done and disbursements made" was inside the meeting room and was not a "towne clock" in the sense of being a tower clock.

Peter Stretch came to Philadelphia in 1702 from Staffordshire, England. His uncle was a famous clockmaker in that country. Stretch prospered in Philadelphia and at the time of his death in 1746 was a man of considerable consequence. His son Thomas Stretch made the State House clock, which was ordered in 1752, six years after the death of the father.

There is additional evidence that there was no public tower clock in Philadelphia before the State House clock. In the late 1740s Benjamin Franklin prevailed upon his friend Edward Duffield to erect a clock in front of the latter's shop at Second and Arch Streets. Franklin and other gentlemen carrying watches had been annoyed by laboring men asking them the time, and with his great ingenuity Franklin felt that a clock visible from the street would put an end to this. Had there been a public tower clock it is not likely that it would have been necessary for an individual clockmaker to have gone to this trouble and expense.

The story of how the weight-and-pendulum clock in a tall case was brought from Holland to England and then from England to Pennsylvania, and how it finally established itself in Pennsylvania, is well told by three clocks now in the possession of the venerable Library Company of Philadelphia, the oldest circulating library in the world in continuous existence, having been founded by Franklin in 1731.

A COMPARATIVE CHRONOLOGY

EARLY PENNSYLVANIA

1638 — Swedes settled on Delaware.

1644 — William Penn born in London. Civil War in England, King versus Parliament.

1655 — Swedish settlements on Delaware passed under Dutch rule. Jamaica seized for the English by Admiral Penn, father of William.

1664 — Dutch rule on Delaware displaced by the English.

1666–1667 — William Penn in Ireland. First contacts with Quakerism. The struggle for tolerance began.

1670 — Death of Admiral Penn, father of William.

CLOCKS

1631 — Clockmakers' Company chartered in London. Domestic lantern, or bracket, clocks common in England. The controlling element was essentially the same as in 1400: crown wheel, verge, and foliot balance.

1658 — Christiaan Huygens announced application of pendulum as controlling element of clock. Huygens still used crown wheel and verge, with pendulum.

1660 — Royal Society in London for Improving Natural Knowledge founded, although informal meetings had been held as early as 1645.

1673 — Huygens published his *Oscillatorium*, fully explaining the theory of the pendulum and clocks.

EARLY PENNSYLVANIA   *CLOCKS*

1675 — Greenwich Observatory founded.

1676 — The anchor escapement invented by Robert Hooke, displacing former verge escapement and introducing seconds pendulum.

1681 — William Penn elected to Royal Society.
Charter for Pennsylvania granted Penn April 2, 1681, "in lieu of Money that was due to (and signal service done by) his father, Sir William Penn."

1682 — Penn landed on Pennsylvania soil, the Commonwealth was set up, and Philadelphia laid out.

1683 — Germantown settled by Germans.

1684 — Penn returned to England.

1687 — Sir Isaac Newton published his *Principia*.

1699 — Penn's second visit to Pennsylvania.

1701 — Penn returned to England.

1714 — Prize offered for "discovery of the longitude at sea" which inspired work on the chronometer.

1715 — The dead beat escapement invented by George Graham.

1718 — William Penn died.

It is often best to permit a clock to tell its own story and it is characteristic of Pennsylvania clocks that most of them have a definite biography. It must always be remembered that the "genealogy" of a clock adds greatly to its value.

The first of these interesting clocks has engraved upon its silvered dial, "Johannes Fromanteel, Londini, fecit." The case is of walnut and has turned columns. This is undoubtedly one of the oldest weight-and-pendulum clocks in a tall case in Pennsylvania today, if not the oldest. So important is this clock that it has received attention from writers on horological subjects abroad, one of whom erroneously states that it belonged to Benjamin Franklin.

The Fromanteel family was very important in the early history of English pendulum clocks. Being of Dutch origin, they brought from Holland to England Huygens's application of the pendulum to clocks.

Johannes Fromanteel was a younger member of this family, and as early as 1657 he went to The Hague to study under a master clockmaker there, returning a year later to pursue his career in London.

The Library Company Fromanteel clock was once owned by Samuel Hudson, a prominent Philadelphian of his time, and after his death in 1793, his son, William Hudson, presented it to the Library.

A notation made in 1804 states that the clock was then "without doubt 140 years old," which is very nearly correct. Ahasuerus Fromanteel, who introduced the pendulum clock in England after the announcement of Huygens in 1658, at first used a short pendulum. Not until the anchor escapement was invented in the 1670s did the long pendulum become practical. Since the Library Company clock has a long pendulum, it would seem to date back to the 1670s. In 1804 the clock was therefore from 125 to 130 years old.

There is an interesting tradition that Samuel Hudson's great-grandfather purchased this clock at an auction sale in London, at which time the auctioneer informed the audience that it had once belonged to Oliver Cromwell. Cromwell died in 1658, the year Huygens announced his invention of the pendulum clock; obviously it could not have belonged to him. It might have belonged to his son Richard Cromwell (b. 1626–d. 1712), who succeeded his father.

This tradition is particularly interesting, since it indicates that even very early in the eighteenth century, weight-and-pendulum clocks in tall cases were being sold at auction in London as "antiques" —and that auctioneers were already making claims not substantiated by facts!

The second clock in the Library Company has engraved upon its square dial, "Wm. Martin, Bristol, fecit." This clock belonged to William Penn himself, who brought it to Pennsylvania on his second visit in 1699 for his manor house at Pennsbury.

William Martin was a clockmaker in Bristol, England. While 1700 is usually given as his date it is apparent that he was working several years before this.

The weight-and-pendulum clock in a tall case was firmly established in England by 1700, and excellent makers were not confined to London. Bristol, for instance, was responsible for some very fine clocks. That Penn had a clock made in Bristol rather than London is not surprising. His father, Admiral Penn, was born in Bristol, and the founder of Pennsylvania had many close ties with that city.

Penn's country home, Pennsbury, was situated on the Delaware in Bucks County, about twenty-four miles from Philadelphia. The site was chosen on his first visit and the house was built by his agents. When he made his second visit in 1699—remaining until 1701—he spent much of his time at Pennsbury, which was handsomely furnished.

After Penn's final return to England, the manor at Pennsbury was abandoned and fell in ruins. The furnishings, including the clock, were scattered. William Penn Warder presented the clock to the Library Company in November 1857.

Pennsbury and its gardens have been restored by the Commonwealth of Pennsylvania through the untiring efforts of several historical groups. A Bristol-made clock of the early 1700s has been placed in the restored manor, but the fact remains that Penn's own clock is in the possession of the Library Company.

The third clock in the Library Company was made by Christopher Sauer about 1735. (The name is variously spelled Saur, Souer, and Sower—but the original form seems to have been Sauer.) This clock is probably the most interesting and valuable of the three, since both works and case were made in Pennsylvania more than two centuries ago.

Not only is it a fine example of clockmaking in early Pennsylvania, but a brief study of the man who made it and his times will help greatly in understanding Philadelphia and Pennsylvania clocks and their makers.

Beginning in 1682 the Quakers settled around Philadelphia. As early as 1683 thirteen German families from the Rhineland settled Germantown. In 1694 a band of mystics came from Germany and established themselves in caves along the Wissahickon. Other Germans came in increasing numbers and from about 1730 until 1750 there was a great influx of the oppressed of Germany, Ireland, and Scotland. This continued up until the Revolution. The Germans sought farm lands in Lancaster County and vicinity, while the Scotch and Irish pushed westward as far as Pittsburgh.

Christopher Sauer was born in Germany in 1693 and came to Philadelphia in the autumn of 1724. He was one of the earlier German immigrants and settled in Germantown, where he worked as a tailor for two years and then bought a farm in the Conestoga Valley. His wife became converted to the teachings of Conrad Beissel, the Seventh Day Adventist who had built the Cloisters at Ephrata. She entered these Cloisters in 1730.

Greatly disturbed by the loss of his wife, Sauer returned to Germantown. He formed an alliance there with Christopher Witt, from whom he learned clockmaking. Witt, of whom later we shall learn more, was a remarkable man.

Clockmaking and repairing were the principal occupations of Sauer for the next few years. Industrious and intelligent, always seeking new intellectual horizons while earning his living by his hands, he afterwards became a printer and publisher of a German newspaper. It has been said that he was proficient in some thirty pursuits; among others were those of farmer, apothecary, surgeon, botanist, clock- and watchmaker, bookbinder, optician, and manufacturer of paper. He drew wire and made the materials for the books he printed. He printed the Bible in German in 1743, some forty years prior to its printing in English in the Colonies. For many years before his death he conducted a shop in Germantown where he sold clocks, medicines, and other wares. He died February 26, 1758.

Penn's clock.

2

THE DIAL OF AHAZ

"Behold, I will bring again the shadow of the degrees, which
is gone down in the sun dial of Ahaz, ten degrees backward.
So the sun returned ten degrees, by which degrees it was
gone down" (Isaiah, 38:8).

VIRTUALLY all books on clocks and
timekeeping refer to the sun dial of Ahaz (or Achaz) as the first time-
indicating device mentioned in the Bible. Known as the Miracle of
Isaiah, the turning backward of time was a sign to Hezekiah, the king,
that fifteen years would be added to his life. Ahaz, in whose reign the
sun dial was constructed, died in 728 B.C., and Hezekiah, his son,
reigned from 715 to 690 B.C. The story of this miracle is also told in
II Kings, 20:9–11.

Today, scholars speculate upon the exact form of the sun dial of
Ahaz of almost twenty-seven centuries ago; there is little authentic
data upon it excepting its mention in the Bible.

There is, however, in the collection of the American Philosophical Society, in Philadelphia, another "Dial of Achaz," or "Horologium Achaz," that is unique. Made in Germany almost four centuries ago, it was brought to Philadelphia before 1700 by men who were to have a profound effect upon clockmaking and science in the Province of Pennsylvania. This instrument is far more than a memento of horology in early Pennsylvania, it is a symbol of the learning possessed by men who often turned their talents to clockmaking and established the science of astronomy in the New World.

The movement which culminated in the astronomical achievements of David Rittenhouse had its beginning in Germany in the latter half of the seventeenth century. There was then much spiritual unrest in Germany. Small groups, dissatisfied with the ritual of the local churches, both Protestant and Catholic, associated themselves under the leadership of learned persons. Most of these groups were of strongly mystical leanings, largely because of the influence of Jacob Boehme, an inspired shoemaker of Silesia. Some groups grew to considerable numbers and it was not long before they came under the ban of the churches.

One group was formed by Philip Jacob Spener, of Dresden and Berlin. Organizations formed under his doctrines were called *Collegia Pietatis* or "Schools of Piety," and their members were known as Pietists. August Hermann Francke, assistant pastor of a church in Erfurt, Thuringia, in about 1690 established a center for Pietists which became a rallying point for mystics all over Germany. Francke, a very learned man, was excommunicated and ordered out of Erfurt; his books were burned and his followers suppressed.

John Jacob Zimmerman, pastor of a church in Württemberg, was an enthusiastic follower of Francke. He was an excellent mathematician and astronomer whose observations had been noticed by the Royal Society. In great distress he appealed to Penn's agent in Rotterdam, Benjamin Furley, asking for asylum in Pennsylvania for himself and his followers. Furley fitted out a ship, arranged for the payment of their passage, and assigned them 2,400 acres of land in Pennsylvania. Zimmerman died on the eve of sailing, but most of his followers embarked for the New World.

A few of Zimmerman's followers, however, went to London,

arriving in August 1693. This group was under the leadership of Johann Kelpius (1673–1708), who at the age of sixteen had graduated from the University of Altdorf, in Bavaria, with the degree of Doctor of Philosophy. However, he was always referred to as Magister, or Master, Kelpius. When Zimmerman organized his "School of Piety" he made himself Master and Kelpius Deputy Master. Kelpius became Master upon Zimmerman's death.

Zimmerman had predicted that the Millennium would come in the autumn of 1694. The group under Kelpius was therefore anxious to start for Pennsylvania and sailed in February of that year. The ship entered the Chesapeake Bay in mid-June and the Pietists landed, making their way overland to Delaware Bay. There they took a sloop for Philadelphia, arriving June 23, 1694. The next day they set out for Germantown. This group of forty men came from all walks of life; most were well grounded in the science of the day.

As soon as possible they retired to the land assigned them some distance from Germantown, where they erected a tabernacle forty feet square surmounted by an astronomical observatory. Here each night an observer watched the heavens for the coming of the Bridegroom. Kelpius took up his abode in a cave, where he lived for fourteen years.

It is difficult today to realize that less than three centuries ago scenes were enacted in what is now part of the city of Philadelphia that hark back to the Middle Ages. The late Julius F. Sachse, the recognized authority on the Pietists, wrote regarding their activities: "The crucible of the alchemist frequently fumed until long after midnight, while the alembic of the Magister was distilling herbs gathered in the dark of the Moon in the hope of discovering the 'Philosopher's Stone' or 'Elixir of Life'—in contrast, as it were, to the lonely watch maintained in the 'Sternwerts' on the lookout for the harbinger of the Bridegroom who was to appear in silky garments."

Although these Pietists mixed learning with mysticism, they were honest in their convictions. True, they studied mathematics in order to calculate the exact time of the Millennium: true, they studied astronomy so that they might be the first to see the coming of the Bridegroom as outlined in the Book of Revelation; yet they had a far wider knowledge of science than any other pioneer group of the time.

While they were hermits in a sense and did not mingle with other settlers, they did establish schools and did have a knowledge of medicine which was very welcome in the community. A learned group such as this had an effect on the surrounding country just as a college or university has on a town today. The group created an atmosphere of learning.

The "Dial of Ahaz" now in the possession of the Philosophical Society undoubtedly belonged to Zimmerman and Kelpius, according to Sachse, who conducted wide research upon the instrument both in Pennsylvania and abroad. It was made in 1578 by Christopher Schissler, a famed instrument maker of Germany, and most probably came to Pennsylvania with the books and other goods of Zimmerman, all of which had been placed on ship board before he died. The seventeenth-century mystic might well see in this device a duplication and explanation of the Miracle of Isaiah.

The instrument is an elaborately made sun dial, the "dial" of which is a basin. When this basin is filled with water the "shadow" or "time" is turned backward ten degrees due to the phenomenon of refraction.

Refraction is simply the bending of a beam of light when it passes from one transparent medium into another, as from air to water. The first written notice of the phenomenon of refraction seems to have been made by Willebrand Snelius (1591–1626) almost half a century after Schissler had demonstrated and used it in his "Dial of Ahaz."

Engraved upon the base of the instrument is a Latin inscription which, when translated, reads, "This semicircular shell explains the miracle of the 38th chapter of Isaiah. For if you will fill the basin with water, the shadow of the sun is borne backwards ten degrees. Moreover, it indicates any common hour together with that of the planets which they call hours."

Several parts of the instrument are now missing, such as the mythological figure which stood on the base and held up the basin: the gnomon or rod used to cast the shadow, as well as the apparatus held aloft by the figure on the rim whereby a thin pencil of light, instead of a shadow, was thrown on the dial. The magnetic needle in the small compass in the base is also missing.

There are today no records of how the instrument originally came into possession of the Society, which was founded by Franklin in 1743, but it is known that upon the death of Kelpius in 1708 his instruments passed into the hands of Daniel Geissler and Christopher Witt. The latter lived until 1765 and was the last survivor of the Pietist group.

Christopher Witt was born in Wiltshire, England, in 1675. Before coming to Pennsylvania in 1704, he had not only become a physician but had delved into occult and practical astronomy. Upon his arrival he joined Kelpius in the caves.

Here Witt painted a portrait of Kelpius in oils in 1706, probably the first oil painting done in the Colonies. This painting is now in the possession of the Historical Society of Pennsylvania. Horologists are interested in the fact that a clock is shown in the background. It may indicate that Witt was making clocks as early as 1706 while still living in the caves with Kelpius and other Pietists. Undoubtedly this is the first representation of a clock in an American painting, and it may be assumed that Witt made the clock himself.

Upon the death of Kelpius, Witt moved into a small house in Germantown and established a botanical garden for the cultivation of medicinal herbs. During the long winters, when it was impossible to roam the fields in search of herbs and plants, he turned to clockmaking. At first he made wall clocks, probably of the type shown in the painting; later he made some very fine tall clocks, a few of which survive.

Witt was an astronomer of no mean ability, but throughout a long and busy life his principal source of income was casting horoscopes for the credulous, and he was known as a *Hexmeister* or "master of spells."

In a previous chapter it has been shown that when Christopher Sauer came to Germantown in 1732, he fell under the influence and patronage of Witt, from whom he learned clockmaking. It may be added that a whole school of clockmakers sprang from Witt, if not directly, then through his influence.

3

THE CLOCKMAKER

PARADOXICAL as it may seem, few who talk or write about clocks and clockmakers have a clear conception of what is meant by the term "clockmaker." Strictly speaking, there are very few clockmakers today; certainly the repairman, no matter how experienced and skillful he may be, cannot be regarded as a clockmaker.

The exact definition of the word puzzled writers more than a century ago. In the 1830s, thousands of clocks were leaving the factories of New England and going to all parts of the world. It is obvious that all who worked in these clock manufactories could not be termed clockmakers.

The subject was handled in a very able manner by a writer in Rees' *Cyclopedia, or Universal Dictionary of Arts, Sciences and Literature*, in an edition published in Philadelphia about 1820. This was when clocks had become so common, "as to be considered an article of household furniture." Also the Pennsylvania tall case clock was being put aside for the cheaper New England clock.

And it was the time when the clockmaker had ceased to be "a man who makes clocks," and the honored term was applied more specifically to the "finisher," the man who "polishes the teeth and steel parts, finishes the pivots, verifies the engagement, adjusts the escapement . . . [adjusts] the maintaining power to the weight of the ball, regulates the adjustments for beat and rate . . . and puts the whole machine in a state ready for sale."

It may be well for us to read the full account in the old "cyclopedia," since it tells us how clockmaking became a specialized endeavor, no longer the craft of one man:

If we were to define the word clock-maker agreeably to the derivation of the term, we should simply say it means a man who makes clocks, and this definition at one period of the art would have been sufficient for our purpose: but since clocks have become so common as to be considered an article of household furniture, the art of making them has not been confined, as at first, to one department of mechanics, but has gradually ramified into various branches, so distinct from one another, that the maker of one part is frequently unacquainted with the operations required for the manipulation of another, equally essential. Since the time that clocks became an article of our manufactories, requiring various tools and engines for facilitating their construction, the subdivision of the art into various departments was a natural consequence, which has been found to contribute to expedition, and consequently to cheapness: and for the same reason that a tailor has no need to understand either spinning, weaving, or dyeing, a finisher of a clock has no occasion to cast or cut his wheels himself, much less to make his springs or enamel his dial-plate. From custom, however, that man is called a clock-maker who finishes or puts together the different constituent parts of a clock when made, and who has his profit from the sale of the machine, though the makers, more properly speaking, are the workmen employed in making the frame and continued wheel work. The different operations may, indeed, be most of them performed by one workman, when the construction is intended to be peculiar, or the works of superior accuracy, but in general the different departments of the art may be separately enumerated agreeably to the subjoined order, viz:

1. The brass-founder casts the wheels, plates, pillars and faces, according to the approved models:
2. The spring-maker forges the shapes and tempers the main-spring to any required strength or dimensions:

3. The making of the weights, to be used as maintaining powers of the balls, or bobs, and the hands, may be considered as one branch:

4. The man who keeps a cutting-engine, and a fusee-engine, cuts the wheels and pinions, and forms the grooves on the fusee or barrel, according as a spring or suspended weight is used as a maintaining power:

5. The movement maker mounts the frame, makes the wheels, pinions, detents, etc., and places them in the frame, agreeable to the proposed calliper:

6. The clock smith forges the steel pieces for the arbors, pinions, pallets, racks, hammers, detents, etc.:

7. The bell-founder casts the bell, or bells when the clock has chimes:

8. The enameller prepares the ground of the dial, or face, for receiving the colour of the figures, and gets the painter to lay on the figures, agreeable to the calliper, with or without a circle for the seconds:

9. When the face is not of real enamel, a japanner, or imitation enameller, prepares and finishes the dial:

10. When the face is brass silvered, an engraver usually prepares, and sometimes silvers it:

11. A jeweller is employed for pallets, and pivot holes of the best astronomical clocks and regulators:

12. The gilder is frequently employed for preparing ornamental parts of the case:

13. The glazier is applied to for the door of the superior part of the cases, when a seconds pendulum is used, and for the principal door sometimes when the clock has a short pendulum:

14. The cabinet maker is resorted to, usually for the case of the clock, and sometimes often the carver:

15. The chain or cat-gut maker is indispensably necessary:

16. Recently the tubular compensation pendulum has been made and adjusted by the mathematical instrument maker, as being a portion that requires great precision:

17. Lastly the finisher, or as he is otherwise called, the maker, polishes the teeth and steel parts, finishes the pivots, verifies the engagement, adjusts the escapement, limits the arc of vibration by adjusting the maintaining power to the weight of the ball, regulates the adjustments for beat and rate, finishes the striking and repeating parts, and puts the whole machine in a state ready for sale.

4

CLOCKMAKERS OF PENNSYLVANIA

In considering an old clock, we cannot divorce it from its maker, for no clock can be better than the skill and patience of the man who made it. There are many good reasons why the Pennsylvania clock today represents the best in early American craftsmanship.

The followers of Penn who first settled in Philadelphia and the adjacent original counties of Bucks and Chester were Quakers. Others who came later were men of the same way of thinking, whether they came from the Rhineland or were Scotch or Irish. All were seeking freedom of worship.

An even greater responsibility than would have been expected of men of this type in a business transaction was engendered between the clockmaker and the original owner of the clock by the fact that they usually knew each other personally and lived together in the same community.

This attitude was well expressed by Isaac Norris when the clock for the State House in Philadelphia was being ordered. In a letter dated

March 10, 1753, he gave the reasons why the clock was to be made in Philadelphia rather than in London. He wrote, "We expect it will prove better than any they would send us from England, where, once they have put it out of their hands, they have done with it; but here the workman would be made very uneasy if he did not exert his utmost skill, as we do not stint him in the price of his labor."

In Pennsylvania more than anywhere else the clock was a symbol of family stability. J. Bennett Nolan, in a charming little book, *The Governor's Clock*, tells how John Andrew Schulze, a Governor of the State, late in life found himself in financial difficulties and asked to retain but one possession—the old family clock made by Valentin Urletig. The Governor's grandfather was Henry Melchior Mühlenberg, the great divine, and the clock had been in the family when Mühlenberg christened his grandson.

So often were family clocks mentioned in wills as possessions of importance to be handed down from generation to generation that they became known as the "grand heirloom."

It is today difficult to appreciate the significance of the role played by the clock in rural Colonial Pennsylvania. The entire life of the farm was regulated by the timepiece in the commodious kitchen, and the care and winding of the clock—they were for the most part 24-hour clocks—became almost a ritual.

In the clocks found on farms, there were often more or less secret devices for controlling the doors covering the faces. There might be a "catch" or hasp that must be first opened, and this would be reached through the panel door. The door, in turn, was fitted with a lock and the key was often left in this lock. However, to open the face glass and regulate the hands it was usually necessary to know the secret method for opening this door. In the finer clocks, those made for mansions in cities where the winding was relegated to a servant, these secret face locks were not often found.

Pennsylvania clockmakers were always men of considerable standing. In Philadelphia they might well be men of affairs and business. Some stood upon an intellectual equality with Franklin and Jefferson. We need mention only David Rittenhouse and Edward Duffield.

Even in rural districts the clockmaker was treated with a respect greater than that accorded the blacksmith, carpenter, or tinsmith and generally not accorded any other class excepting the doctor or minister.

This is not difficult to understand if we look back two centuries or so. What then were the outlets for the ingenuity of a boy with a mechanical and mathematical mind? Today such a boy would find many places in engineering and industry, but two centuries ago clockmaking, and possibly surveying, were the only avenues open.

It would be difficult to mention a man in England or America in the late eighteenth century or early nineteenth who stands out in the history of scientific or mechanical achievement, without finding that he began as a clockmaker or at least showed great interest in clocks.

This was particularly true in Pennsylvania, where clocks and their makers were part of a people. Pennsylvania demanded thoroughness on the part of its clockmakers. No great clock factories were ever established in the Province or State, and the few attempts to do so met with vigorous opposition.

John Fitch had served his apprenticeship with a clockmaker in New England, but whatever practical success his steamboat achieved was largely due to a Pennsylvania clockmaker—Henry Voight. Later, Matthias Baldwin and Phineas Davis were clockmakers but when their ambitions soared they did not establish large clock factories but turned to building locomotives.

Clockmaking in Pennsylvania was a highly honorable calling. David Rittenhouse pursued it all his life, while becoming one of the really great scientists of his time. And Benjamin Franklin invented a three-wheel clock.

Many years ago it was the author's privilege to know a clockmaker of the old Pennsylvania school, B. T. Schmauk, whose experience then reached back seventy years. He had served his apprenticeship under men who had served theirs, in turn, under the earlier masters.

Mr. Schmauk outlined for the author what was required of an apprentice. His first task, as a boy, was to cut hands out of thin sheet metal. The clockmaker scribed the outlines of the hands upon the metal, and the boy cut these with a saw and filed and polished them.

It was not the production of hands that was important—it was testing the apprentice's patience and native skill. But the master was thrifty; while the boy was being tested he was still producing some-thing worth while. Machines can cut clock hands by the thousands, but no machine can teach a boy those qualities which later, as a man, he will put into his clocks.

When he had mastered the cutting and finishing of hands, the boy was given other small parts to make. Then he was given a clock to take apart. To do this properly is no less exacting than to put it together again. By his approach to this task the boy indicated to his master whether or not he had the aptitude for becoming a clockmaker. Many showed they would never master the craft and were eliminated.

Others showed patience and skill and went forward. The old clockmakers of Pennsylvania served a hard apprenticeship and upon its completion usually set up business for themselves. Only a young man with a strong inclination for the work would survive the apprentice-ship. Clockmaking called to itself men who would make good clocks—those who were not adapted soon dropped out. Only the best survived.

It is true that clockmakers in Pennsylvania often bought wheels, plates, and other parts which they finished and built into clocks. But it was never a matter of mass production, since every clock was an indi-vidual effort. An average clockmaker in Pennsylvania might make four or five clocks a year. Had he been able to make more it is improbable that he could have disposed of them. The Pennsylvania clock repre-sented quite an outlay of money and was usually the only timekeeper in a dwelling.

The fact that Pennsylvania makers often bought parts, usually imported from England, has been given too much emphasis by present-day writers. What these men bought was far indeed from a finished clock. And even though a clockmaker could buy parts his resource-fulness was often taxed. In days when transportation was difficult and uncertain, a man would often make a required part rather than wait for it. Frequently he beat out his brass plates or even substituted iron.

In considering the Pennsylvania clock we must look upon the works and the case separately. The cabinetmakers who made the cases displayed great skill, and their work varies from good carpentry to the finest cabinet work. But whether the case is beautifully made along classic lines, or a clumsy attempt at classic lines by some less skilled craftsman, it largely reflects the character of the original owner for whom it was made.

DAVID RITTENHOUSE

No history of science in America could be written without mention of the greatest Pennsylvania clockmaker—David Rittenhouse. He stands out as a man of broad genius and accomplishment —and yet was an example of a large group of Pennsylvania clockmakers of his own time and later, who combined science with craftsmanship.

In this group belong Edward Duffield, friend of Franklin and member of the American Philosophical Society; Joseph Ellicott and his son Andrew, who became surveyor general of the United States and professor of mathematics at West Point; Henry Voight, first coiner of the United States Mint, to whom much of the success achieved by John Fitch's steamboat must be credited; Isaiah Lukens, town clockmaker and honored member of the Philosophical Society, the Academy of Natural Sciences, and the Franklin Institute; Joseph Saxton, who had a brilliant career abroad and returned to work with the United States Coast Survey, and Jacob D. Custer, who made clocks and was a pioneer in making lighthouse equipment.

Much has been written about clockmakers in Pennsylvania in an effort to establish where they learned their craft and what sort of men they were. Since Rittenhouse was the outstanding clockmaker in Pennsylvania, let us examine his background and how he arrived at his place among men of learning.

Benjamin Franklin, John Winthrop, and David Rittenhouse have been called "the philosophical trio of the Revolution." Little need be said about Franklin, since his story has often been told. John Winthrop, of Harvard, was "heir to the riches of transplanted European scholarship." Rittenhouse was a self-made astronomer, "a true product of American genius and toil—the highest embodiment of the pioneer spirit in science during the Colonial period." This might also be said of many other Pennsylvania clockmakers.

To understand the background of Rittenhouse is to understand early American courage and skill in science and industry. His ancestor,

William Rittenhouse, was a papermaker and in 1690, together with others, founded the first paper mill in the Colonies at Germantown. William Rittenhouse and his son Claus (Nicholas) soon bought out their cofounders.

In 1700 the Rittenhouses met with disaster when the mill was carried away by a freshet. The loss was regarded as so great a blow to the future of Pennsylvania that William Penn sent out an appeal for help to rebuild it, and himself headed the subscription.

William Rittenhouse, the papermaker, was the first bishop of the Mennonite Church. He died in 1708 and was succeeded by his son Claus, who died in 1743. Claus Rittenhouse was the grandfather of the astronomer and clockmaker.

David Rittenhouse was born on April 8, 1732, the year of Washington's birth, in a small house in Germantown which is still standing. His father abandoned papermaking, the traditional occupation of the family, and moved to a farm at Norriton, about twenty miles from Philadelphia, when David was two years old. The family was not wealthy, but was in comfortable circumstances.

The boy seemed destined to the life of a farmer. At the age of twelve, however, he received a bequest of tools and mathematical books from an uncle and these aroused his interest. It was not long before his mechanical skill was turned to clockmaking.

His Mennonite ancestry had an important bearing upon the career of David Rittenhouse, as it had upon many other Pennsylvania clockmakers. The Mennonites were not traders and men of commerce, but thrifty, self-contained people who asked little of the world and wanted only to be left alone to worship God as they saw fit. They never dreamed of glory and profit, nor did they have any desire to build up large industries and fortunes upon the efforts of others.

It was significant that David Rittenhouse was born in Germantown. We have seen how the mystics there—Kelpius, Witt, and others —were delving into astronomy in the very early eighteenth century. Witt was alive when Rittenhouse was born, and lived for some years thereafter. Science, astronomy, and clockmaking were not unfamiliar to the people of Germantown, thanks to Witt and the men associated with him. Rittenhouse was only two when his family moved from Germantown to Norriton, but there were still close family contacts between the two places.

In 1749, when only seventeen, Rittenhouse had established himself at Norriton as the maker of accurate clocks. These early clocks are well and skillfully made and show no crudity. It is absurd to seek early "crude" Rittenhouse clocks, because none was ever made. Rittenhouse showed skill and finish from the beginning.

The year 1751 was an important one in Rittenhouse's life, because Thomas Barton, a graduate of Trinity College, Dublin, came to Norriton to teach school. He afterwards married a sister of Rittenhouse. Barton was an energetic and restless man, and in a letter to him in 1767 Rittenhouse first described his plans for an orrery, a clockwork model of the planetary system.

In 1770 Rittenhouse moved to Philadelphia, where he took his place among the foremost scientific men of America. In the following year he became secretary of the American Philosophical Society and later succeeded Franklin as president. (He was himself succeeded by Thomas Jefferson in that office.) Clockmaking continued to be his chief source of income, and his orders for clocks always exceeded his capacity to fill them.

He was married twice. In 1766 he married Eleanor Colston, daughter of a neighboring Quaker farmer. She died shortly after he moved to Philadelphia. In 1772 he married Hannah Jacobs. His two daughters by his first marriage survived Rittenhouse.

Rittenhouse's first residence in Philadelphia was at the southeast corner of Seventh and Arch Streets. On the northwest corner, diagonally opposite, he built an octagonal brick observatory. This was the first, and for many years the only, astronomical observatory in America.

He died June 26, 1796, and was buried under the observatory. Later his body was removed to the cemetery of Old Pine Street Presbyterian Church, and finally, in 1878, was interred in North Laurel Hill Cemetery.

Aside from their pervasively accurate and careful workmanship, it may be safely said that there is no one characteristic common to all David Rittenhouse clocks. Each of his timepieces represented an individual effort, deliberately planned and perfectly executed.

The number of clocks made by Rittenhouse in his entire lifetime was not great, perhaps not more than seventy-five. Some of these have disappeared. Of the clocks remaining today, virtually every one has a pedigree going back to its original owner.

Here it may be well to remark that the clocks of David Rittenhouse are not to be confused with those of his younger brother Benjamin, himself a man of ability but greatly overshadowed by David. Benjamin's clocks bear the place name "Worcester," the neighboring township to Norriton, the place name which appears on many David Rittenhouse clocks.

The signature of David Rittenhouse on his clocks shows a considerable variety of styles, since he used both the new and the old-fashioned "s." The former was just coming into vogue and was neither consistently nor universally used.

There is, of course, no uniformity in the wooden cases, which were supplied by many different cabinetmakers. It is impossible to formulate any universal recipe for easy identification of authentic David Rittenhouse clocks. Each example must be studied on its own merits and not as one of a multitude of standardized articles turned out on a production basis.

Probably the best approach to the clocks of David Rittenhouse is through study of the two orreries he made. The first was made for Princeton College. It disappeared many years ago but has been recently discovered and is now restored. The second, made for the University of Pennsylvania, was restored some years ago and is now a cherished possession of that institution.

The latter instrument aroused great excitement in its time. Thomas Jefferson wrote of it, "A machine far surpassing in ingenuity of contrivance, accuracy, and utility, anything of the kind ever before constructed . . . He has not indeed made a world, but by imitation approached nearer its Maker than any man who has lived from the creation to this day."

Never numerous, even in the man's own time, Rittenhouse clocks are today almost unobtainable. Their inevitable drift is toward a permanent place in museums, and those in the hands of private collectors are destined to find their way to institutions of arts or science. Occasionally an example is offered for sale, but it will seldom be one that has not suffered from undesirable tampering. An authentic example may be classed among the gems of craftsmanship that are the goal of a collector's ambition.

Astronomical clock built
by David Rittenhouse.

5

THE "RULES AND REASON" OF PENNSYLVANIA CLOCKS

AFTER more than two and a half centuries the weight-and-pendulum clock in a tall case is still the best-designed mechanical device for accurate timekeeping. Powered and controlled by the inexorable force of gravity, honest and rugged in construction, these clocks were taken unto themselves by the people of Pennsylvania.

To appreciate fully the clocks, the men who made them, and the people for whom they were made, we should know, as did the old clockmakers, "the Reason for their own Rules that govern their excellent workmanship." William Penn, in his *Reflections and Maxims*, stated that the artificer who knew the reason of the rules that governed his work was a "compleat Mechanick." The clockmakers of Pennsylvania were "compleat" in this sense.

So much has been written about the theory and practice of clockmaking that most people fear even to begin looking into the rules, to say nothing of the reason behind these rules. There is no sound basis for this fear. Anyone, with very little effort, can understand both the rules and reason.

In the final analysis, these clocks are simply machines designed and built to maintain and record the swings of a pendulum. It will serve our purpose at this point to state that the characteristic of the pendulum which gives it a supreme place in clock mechanism is the fact that a pendulum of a certain length will swing in equal periods of time, the periods being dependent upon the length of the pendulum. Thus a pendulum 39.14 inches long, the one almost always found in tall case clocks, will take one second to swing from right to left, and another second to return, and so on.

This is the condensed and greatly simplified statement of a physical law. Theoretically, a pendulum once started will continue to swing indefinitely. In practice, however, the pendulum encounters friction at the point of suspension and resistance from the air through which it swings. These elements, if not compensated for, would not only vary the periods of swing but would ultimately bring the pendulum to rest.

Galileo and others actually had assistants give the pendulum the necessary impulses by hand to keep it swinging when they made astronomical observations.

The purpose of applying weights to the clock mechanism was to supply the amount of energy lost through friction.

A pendulum alone would not indicate and record time. Hence it was necessary to supply indicating devices, known as hands, which, through the train or wheel work, moved in accordance with the swings of the pendulum.

The power mechanism—the weight—acts through the train to keep the pendulum in motion: while the pendulum, through the escapement, reacts upon the power mechanism so as to expend the energy in uniform and equally divided amounts at exact intervals, namely, at each swing.

For simplicity, accuracy, and efficiency, the weight as motive power and the pendulum as the regulating medium constitute the best-known combination for stationary clocks.

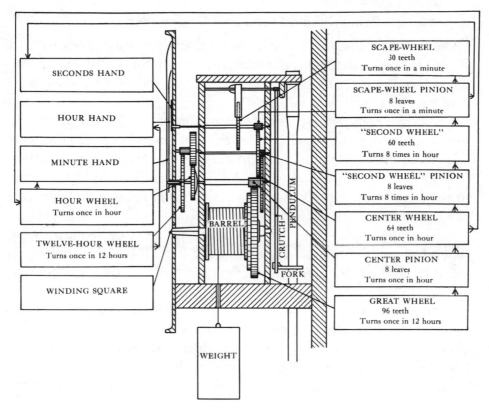

SECONDS HAND	SCAPE-WHEEL 30 teeth Turns once in a minute
HOUR HAND	SCAPE-WHEEL PINION 8 leaves Turns once in a minute
MINUTE HAND	"SECOND WHEEL" 60 teeth Turns 8 times in hour
HOUR WHEEL Turns once in hour	"SECOND WHEEL" PINION 8 leaves Turns 8 times in hour
TWELVE-HOUR WHEEL Turns once in 12 hours	CENTER WHEEL 64 teeth Turns once in hour
WINDING SQUARE	CENTER PINION 8 leaves Turns once in hour
	GREAT WHEEL 96 teeth Turns once in 12 hours

BARREL — CRUTCH — PENDULUM — FORK — WEIGHT

Schematic diagram of eight-day
weight-and-pendulum clock.

Fundamentally these clocks consist of four parts:

1. THE WEIGHT: which is the source of power.
2. THE TRAIN: which transmits the downward pull of the weight into rotary velocity.
3. THE ESCAPEMENT: which transmits the rotary velocity of the train into intermittent—or periodic—motion.
4. THE PENDULUM: which is the controlling element associated with the intermittent motion of the escapement.

THE WEIGHT AS MOTIVE POWER

The weight is the cheapest and most dependable motive power for a stationary clock, in which it is superior to a spring. The force of a spring may vary with its tension but the force of a weight is constant.

Here the value of a tall case for a clock may be seen clearly. In short cramped cases there is insufficient room for a full fall of the weight, and changes must be made in the construction of the clock to compensate for the short fall.

Theoretically, a clock can be constructed to run any length of time by increasing the number of wheels and pinions between the great wheel and the center pinion and increasing the weight in proportion.

However, the chances of error due to imperfections in the shape of the teeth of the wheels and from variations in friction are increased as the number of wheels is increased.

Everything else being equal, the timekeeper that requires being wound oftenest is most likely to run the best. But this advantage is offset by the fact that frequent winding increases the risk of disturbing the rate of the clock.

Once a week was hit upon as a happy medium—since the beginning or ending of a week is a time not likely to be forgotten. One day was added for safety. This is why tall clocks are usually of the eight-day variety. There was ample room in the tall case to permit the weight a full drop for that length of time without complicating matters with additional wheels.

There is an interesting interrelationship among the four parts of the clock—the weight, the train, the escapement and the pendulum.

First, it is upon the pendulum, and the pendulum alone, that the clock relies for accurately measuring time.

No special property can be imparted to the escapement which, in itself, will produce good timekeeping. A badly constructed escapement will produce irregular timekeeping, but the most accurate escapement cannot bring about any better timekeeping qualities than the accuracy of the construction and adjustment of the pendulum permit.

And by the same token, no special arrangement of wheel work can create power. Badly arranged wheel work can destroy power, but the best-arranged train cannot create any more power than the weight supplies.

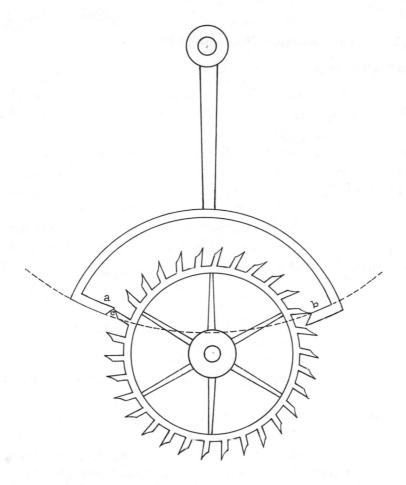

George Graham had one of his escapements applied to a clock before the year 1720. This diagram is an exact representation of Graham's escapement as originally made for him by John Shelton. The description of the action is best given in the words of the inventor: "The tooth *c* having just escaped from the pallet *a*, the opposite pallet instantly receives the full shock of the tooth *b* on its circular arc; the vibration proceeding, this pallet enters deep between the teeth, but not so far as to touch the bottom, the swing (scape) wheel and second-hand remaining motionless till, by the succeeding vibration, the tooth *b* is brought to the edge of the inclined plane of its pallet, at which instant it begins to act, pushing away the pallet till it escapes at the lower point, when immediately another tooth, striking on the circular part of the other pallet, rides at rest upon it until the inclined plane begins to present itself, and then following the slope of the pallet, pushes it away, and at last escapes, as did the first tooth *c*; and so on."

THE PENDULUM

The pendulum is not a showy appendage of the clock. Rather, the clock is an appendage of the pendulum. Yet few understand the theory and practice of the pendulum.

Turning to the theoretical discussion of the pendulum, and the application of theory to practice, we begin to appreciate the ingenuity and learning of the men who made the weight-and-pendulum mechanism possible.

While the honor of first suggesting the use of the pendulum for timekeeping is usually given to Galileo, Asiatic astronomers long before him measured the duration of eclipses by counting the swings of a pendulum.

Huygens was probably the first actually to apply a pendulum to a clock, and we are certain that he was the first to explain and understand fully the mathematical theories involved.

For all practical purposes, it is the length of the pendulum that is important in clockmaking, since the length determines the period or time of swing.

The practical clockmaker or repairman does not attempt to time the individual swings of a given pendulum in seconds. He counts the ticks per minute. There is one tick for each swing of the pendulum in a clock. That is, there is one tick when the pendulum swings from right to left, then another when it swings from left to right, and so on.

In the tall case clock, with a 39.14-inch pendulum in perfect adjustment, there will be sixty ticks per minute, which means that the pendulum takes one second for each swing.

Tables are available in clockmakers' handbooks showing the comparison between the number of swings per minute and the respective lengths of pendulums.* In most handbooks the word "vibrations" is

---

* The length of a pendulum is the distance between the point of suspension and a point known as the center of oscillation. In the theoretical simple pendulum of the mathematician, the center of gravity and center of oscillation of the pendulum are the same. In the material pendulum of the clockmaker this is not so. In the material pendulum the center of oscillation is not even always at a fixed point but varies in relation to the part where the suspension spring of the pendulum bends. For all practical purposes, in a wood rod pendulum, of about 10 pounds weight, the center of gravity is about 0.8 inch above the center of the ball and the center of oscillation is about 0.1 inch above the center of the ball. The length of a pendulum

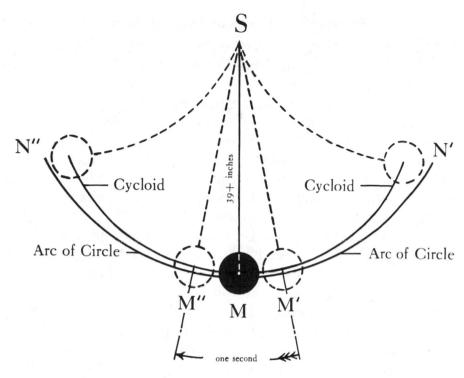

The simple pendulum consists, basically, of a bob M suspended from a point S. When the bob is lifted to M'—and released—the earth pulls it downward, and by virtue of this pull it swings to M and continues to M". The bob then proceeds over the same course backwards, and this to-and-fro motion is repeated until it is stopped by the resistance of the air and by friction at the point S.

used for swings. This is not strictly correct, since a vibration is a complete cycle, from right to left and back again—actually two swings. However, the use of the word "vibration" for swing goes back to 1667 in writings of the Royal Society, so we must accept it.

Sixty swings (ticks) per minute indicates a pendulum 39.14 inches long, the famous "seconds" pendulum usually found in tall case clocks. Eighty swings (ticks) per minute indicates a pendulum 22.01 inches long, the one usually found in banjo clocks. One hundred and twenty swings (ticks) per minute indicates a pendulum 9.78 inches long, the "half seconds pendulum" often found in New England shelf clocks.

Counting ticks per minute and bringing a clock to time by adjusting the nut which supports the bob of a pendulum is a simple process.

is the distance from the point of suspension to a point near the center of the bob or ball, not to the bottom of the bob or ball.

But we must never forget that every clock was originally designed and built largely around a pendulum of predetermined length and not the other way about.

It has been said that calculating the length of a pendulum is today something that most people know and care little about. The collector is usually concerned only about having the "original" pendulum in his clock. The repairman is concerned only with the adjustment necessary to bring the clock to time, the actual length of the pendulum meaning little or nothing to him. People who take these attitudes blind themselves to the real pleasures of horology.

To avoid confusion at the very beginning of our discussion on calculating the length of a pendulum, we must realize that the mathematician deals with what he calls a simple pendulum, a theoretical pendulum in which the mass of the bob is concentrated at one point, its center, and the bob suspended by a cord or rod of no appreciable weight. We need not be disturbed too deeply about all this, because there is little difference between the actual and the theoretical.

Every textbook on physics gives a mathematical formula for calculating the length of a pendulum for any given period, or time, of swing. Unfortunately, many clockmakers and collectors today look upon this formula with dismay. Let us look at it a moment and try to understand it.

The mathematician regards the period of oscillation of a pendulum as the time for a full cycle, that is, from right to left and back again. This is just twice as long as the period of the clockmaker's swing. Therefore many books give the formula as follows:

$$t = 2\pi \sqrt{\frac{l}{g}}$$

In this case, the period of time is for a full cycle. We will use the formula for a single swing, however, from right to left or left to right. This is:

$$t = \pi \sqrt{\frac{l}{g}}$$

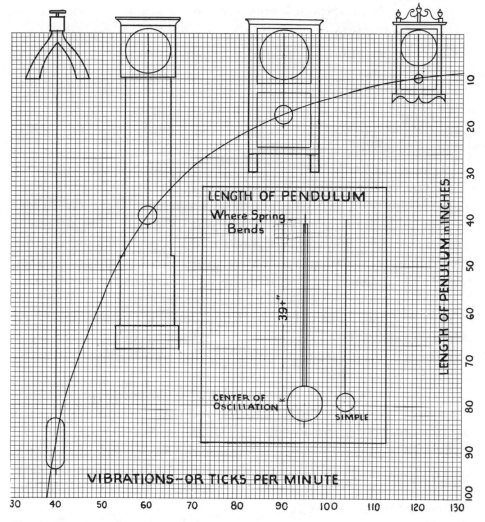

Chart showing relationship between lengths of clock pendulums and their respective periods of vibration (ticks per minute). Inset shows what is meant by length of a clock (material) pendulum. From left to right is first shown the pendulum of a tower clock. Next is shown schematically the weight-and-pendulum clock in a tall case; these clocks almost invariably having the famous seconds pendulum. Then is shown a New England shelf clock in boxlike case. Finally the "Pillar Scroll Top Case" clock is shown which is fitted with a half-second pendulum.

t stands for period of swing in seconds, that is, the time for one swing of the pendulum from right to left, or left to right. It is equivalent to the number of ticks per minute divided by sixty.

π is the constant 3.1416, which takes care of "circular" motion, as the pendulum bob swings in a path which is an arc of a circle.

l is the length of pendulum in feet. If the answer is desired in inches, this must be multiplied by twelve.

g represents "acceleration due to gravity." The value of *g* varies for different places on the earth's surface and for varying heights above sea level. However, 32.2 feet "per second, per second" is a fair figure. The pendulum bob "falls" due to the force of gravity, the attraction between the earth and the bob. The force of this attraction, and the acceleration due to it, *g*, varies to a small extent with the distance between the center of the bob and that of the earth itself.

For this reason a pendulum beating seconds in London will be 39.14 inches long, while in Havana, Cuba, nearer the equator, it will be only 39.05 inches long. Strangely enough, these apparently very slight differences in length are important in making adjustments when accurate timekeeping is desired.

There remains but one more feature of the pendulum that perplexes many people. Scientists have proved that, for a pendulum "to secure uniformity in time of its oscillations no matter how wide the arc of swing," the bob must pursue the path of a curve known as a *cycloid*. Again, the practical came to the rescue of the theoretical because if the arc of swing is small there is little difference between the cycloid and the arc of a circle.

When the weight-and-pendulum clock in a tall case was first thought of, the essential feature was a pendulum of a certain length with a fixed period of swing. Fortunately it was found that a pendulum 39.14 inches long, the ideal length for these clocks, would have a period of one second. The invention of the anchor escapement in the 1670s made a small arc of swing possible.

These clocks kept excellent time, largely because the design of the pendulum, simple and quite easy to make and adjust, conformed very closely to the requirements of higher mathematics and physics.

6

THE ALMANAC BUILT IN A CLOCK

Of all the heavenly bodies, the moon has always been second only to the sun in interest. Today it is difficult to realize the importance attached to the ever-changing phases of the moon in times past. Totally aside from the superstitions and folk-lore that attached themselves to the moon, it must be remembered that travel and outdoor endeavors at night were hazardous undertakings two centuries and more ago. It was important to know how much moonlight might be expected on a certain date.

The almanac, or astronomical diary, containing information about the heavenly bodies and their movements, including the moon, was a common book in Pennsylvania. In 1685 William Bradford published the first American almanac. His *Kalendarium Pennsilvaniense, or America's Messinger*, published in Philadelphia, was an almanac for the year 1686.

In about 1730, clockmakers began building "almanacs" into their clocks, whereby the phase of the moon might be ascertained at a glance and predictions made whether much or little moonlight might be expected on a certain night in the near future. This invention was not made in Pennsylvania, but it was soon adopted and became very popular.

Today most collectors and owners of clocks fitted with the moon device look upon the arrangement as a decorative feature rather than an important adjunct to the clock. Some have even had it disconnected from the driving mechanism. This is to be regretted, since the moon device is part of the clock itself and an understanding of its working and adjustment will add greatly to the interest in the clock.

The clockmakers endeavored to simulate and approximate the appearance of the moon in the heavens. The phases, or changes, of the moon have been described as the different forms which its visible disc presents to the earth: New Moon, First Quarter, Full Moon and Last Quarter. Of course these terms are purely arbitrary, since the moon is constantly changing.

The interval from New Moon to New Moon is known as the lunar month and is approximately 29½ days. Actually the lunar month is 29 days, 12 hours, 44 minutes and 2.8 seconds. The "Age of the Moon" is the time elapsed from New Moon in any lunar month.

Just what celestial phenomenon was it that these old clockmakers were endeavoring to depict on a clock dial? When the moon is in conjunction with the earth, that is, directly between the sun and earth, the "enlightened" half of the moon is away from the earth and the moon is invisible. (The moon has no light of its own but merely reflects light from the sun.) This is known as New Moon and there is no moonlight. The almanacs usually show this as a solid black disc ●.

A little less than 7½ days later, one half of the moon's illuminated surface is visible to the earth and it appears as a semicircle. This is known as First Quarter and is designated in the almanac by a crescent ❭.

Then, about 7½ days later, or a little less than 15 days from New Moon, the whole of the moon's illuminated surface is turned toward the earth and the moon appears as a full circle of light. This is known as Full Moon and it is the time of maximum moonlight. The almanacs show Full Moon * as a circle ○.

---

* Strictly speaking, and according to the U.S. government style manual and others, Full Moon is properly shown by symbol ○, a circle with no center dot. ⊙ is the sun. Unfortunately, some old almanacs used both symbols interchangeably.

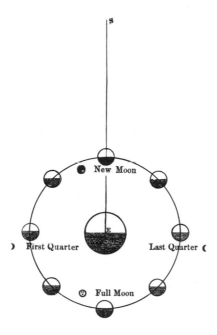

The moon's phases are accounted for by assuming it to be an opaque globular body, rendered visible by the reflection of light received from the sun. This drawing shows the earth E and the orbit of the moon, the sun being supposed to be at a great distance S. When the moon is in conjunction, the enlightened half is turned directly from the earth, and it is then invisible and is called New Moon.

About 7½ days after New Moon, when the moon is in quadrature, one half of its illuminated surface is turned toward the earth, and the enlightened disc appears as a semicircle. The moon is then at First Quarter.

About 15 days after New Moon, when it is in opposition, the whole of the illumined surface is turned toward the earth and the moon appears as a full circle. It is then Full Moon.

About 7½ days after this, when the moon is again in quadrature, one half of the illumined surface being toward the earth, it again appears as a semicircle. It is then at Last Quarter.

(Drawing adapted from *An Elementary Treatise on Astronomy*, John Gummere, Haverford School, Pennsylvania, 1842. Published by E. C. & J. Biddle, Philadelphia.)

About 7½ days after Full Moon, only one half of the illuminated surface of the moon is visible. This is known as Last Quarter and is designated in the almanacs by a crescent ☾ .

The old clockmakers, with their knowledge of astronomy and almanacs, knew all this. Their goal was to build an almanac into the clock so that it would be unnecessary to consult a book to ascertain the age of the moon. The problem resolved itself into two parts, (a) where to place the "almanac" on the clock face and (b) how to plan the mechanism and presentation.

The first part of the problem was solved by the development of the clock dial itself. The earliest clocks had square dials. The arched dial was introduced about the beginning of the eighteenth century. This made a semicircle available above the square dial proper. At first the space within this semicircle had a cartouche bearing the maker's name.

The minds of the old clockmakers were both ingenious and restless, and the semicircle above the dial proper was a challenge. In 1720, or thereabouts, moving figures began to appear in this space, figures which moved back and forth with the swings of the pendulum. They took the forms of prancing deer, rocking ships, Father Time and his scythe, and such. While they were of no practical value they did give a pleasing element of motion and life.

Now that motion had been introduced in the semicircle above the dial, it became obvious that this was the ideal place to reproduce the progress from New Moon to New Moon. Some very ingenious mechanisms were evolved with accuracy as their goal, but eventually one system became the most popular and, it may be said, "standard." This was only an approximation, but sufficiently accurate for everyday purposes. It was based upon a lunar month of 29½ days.

Two Full Moons were painted upon a "moon wheel," diametrically opposite each other. Two hemispheres, or circles that were painted to depict the hemispheres, became part of the dial proper. These were so laid out that at a certain position, New Moon, both moons on the moon wheel were exactly obscured behind their respective hemispheres.

The moon wheel was so arranged that one moon would emerge

from behind the hemisphere on the left and travel a semicircular path until it was finally hidden by the hemisphere on the right. Then the second moon would emerge from the hemisphere on the left and the drama would be reenacted.

Of course the moons usually had human faces, to carry on the legend of the "Man in the Moon." Another decorative feature was a landscape painted on one half of the moon wheel and a seascape on the other half—symbols of land and sea.

When the moon wheel had been worked out in principle, the next step was to achieve a close approximation of accuracy. This was done by placing 118 teeth on the moon wheel, 59 teeth for each lunar month. The socket of the hour hand of the clock was so engaged that one tooth of the moon wheel moved forward for every complete revolution of the hour hand—once every twelve hours. Thus it will be seen that the moon wheel operated on a 29½ day lunar month.

Now the actual lunar month is 44 minutes and 2.8 seconds longer than the time made by the moon wheel. Therefore, in one year the moon wheel will have gained over nine hours. This should be compensated for. In actual practice the clockmakers sometimes instructed their customers to set the moon wheel back about nine hours every year, or about one day in three years.

It is important to remember that when the clock is started it is necessary to set the moon wheel independently of the clock itself. In short, setting the moon wheel is an independent project. The fact that a clock keeps accurate time does not mean that the moon wheel is in phase with the moon itself.

An almanac should be consulted to set the moon wheel. These books give the day and hour of New Moon, etc. With this information it is possible to push the moon wheel forward by hand until it is in phase with the moon. Many calendars give information as to the phases of the moon. These may be used if no almanac is available.

The moon wheel is ingenious, interesting, and accurate enough for all practical purposes. But at its best it is only an approximation, and while it serves its purpose for everyday needs it is not an astronomical instrument. It opened a wide field of decoration for clock dials. Color was added to the sometimes drab brass and silvered dials. At first the heavens on the wheel might be painted blue, with gold stars added for effect. Artists added some very creditable paintings.

The late Dr. Edwin Miller Fogel collected many of the beliefs of the Pennsylvania Germans and published them. It may be well to present a few of the beliefs regarding the moon so that the importance of the lunar phases to these people may be appreciated.

Sweep the house in the dark of the moon (New Moon) and you will have neither moths nor spiders.

Shingle the roof in the decrease of the moon (between Full Moon and the next New Moon) so that the shingles are put on when the horns of the moon are turned down, and they will warp and rise up. The same holds good for boardwalks.

The number of snows during winter is indicated by the number of days from the first snow in fall to the following Full Moon.

Trees planted at Full Moon will bear very well.

Plant peas and potatoes in the increase of the moon.

The meat of animals slaughtered in the increase of the moon will not shrink in the pot or in curing.

The Pennsylvania German also used his clock as a weather prophet, since one of his beliefs was: "If a clock with brass works ticks very loud it is a sign of stormy weather."

There is a basis of scientific fact in this belief. Sound waves are better transmitted in a dense and damp atmosphere than in a dry atmosphere. Hence a clock would tick louder before a storm.

7

REPAIR AND RESTORATION

IT is important that the owner—and prospective owner—of a Pennsylvania clock know something about repair and restoration. This knowledge is valuable even though he has no intention of attempting the work himself. With it, he will be able to form his own estimate as to how much of a clock is original and how much has been changed and added through the years. Above all else, this knowledge will add to his pleasure of ownership.

That a clock is running and keeping time is, in itself, no true indication of its actual condition. The Pennsylvania clock is remarkable in that if it is put together with only moderate accuracy, set going under fairly favorable conditions, and wound regularly, it will run itself to pieces before stopping.

On the other hand, there has never been a Pennsylvania clock, no matter how old, that could not be put in condition with judicious care and serve for many years more in preserving the hallowed memories associated with it.

Some of these clocks have been badly handled by repairmen. This damage may have happened years ago. As early as 1872 a writer in *The American Horological Journal* * stated:

Very few of the younger portion of this generation of watchmakers, wherever they may have served their apprenticeship, have had sufficient opportunities afforded them to learn to repair one of these clocks: we know of only one large firm in the country where they are thoroughly and conscientiously repaired with a view to restore them to their original condition and in repairing study to retain as much of the old parts as is possible; for when the clocks are relics, their owners generally desire this to be scrupulously attended to.

Great care must be exercised in the choice of a clockmaker to repair and restore these clocks. Not every clock- and watchmaker, however familiar he may be with modern timepieces, is fitted by training and experience to undertake this work. Fortunately today, with little searching, men may be found in every city and community who can do the work in a satisfactory manner. This is largely due to an increased interest in the clocks and a realization of their value.

It is the purpose of this chapter to make it possible for the owner to judge clockmakers as well as clocks. With a basic knowledge of repairs and restoration an owner can protect his clock from damage in the hands of an unskilled workman.

It is fortunate that many years ago a clockmaker's apprentice wrote his reminiscences; † with his help we can serve our own apprenticeships in clockmaking quickly and without drudgery. And we too can benefit from the experience and wisdom of his master.

REMOVING A CLOCK FROM ITS CASE

Naturally the first step is to learn how to remove a clock from its tall case. Regarding this our apprentice wrote:

---

* *The American Horological Journal* made its first appearance in July 1869. The editor and publisher was G. B. Miller, and the office of publication was at 229 Broadway, New York City. Its contributors were some of the "brightest lights of the horological firmament" both in America and Europe. The *Journal* appeared monthly and contained thirty-two pages of practical reading matter of the highest order and little or no advertising. The last issue was for the month of August 1873.

† "Reminiscences of an Apprentice," *American Horological Journal*, New York, 1869, etc. These articles were probably written by Napoleon B. Sherwood.

He [the master] was as particular about my motions, when he taught me to take such clocks as I speak of, out of the case, as the drill sergeant afterwards was with us when going through platoon exercise after I joined the Volunteers.

He would place his right knee on the front of the case, and slide the head gently off with his hands, first examining if all the wood-work of the head of the case was firm, lest, if in the act of taking it off, the head might fall out of his hands.

Then he would examine the suspension of the pendulum, to see if the back-fork fitted to the pendulum properly. Next he would take the pendulum off, catching ahold of it with one hand a little above the middle, and with the other hand disengage it from the suspension, and let it slide down and settle comfortably in the bottom of the case, leaning it in a corner at the back, if it had not to be taken away.

Next the weights were taken off by catching the pulley with one hand, and unhooking the weight with the other; but before doing so, I had to put my hand on the seat board, lest the clock tumble down when the weights were taken off, should it be badly fitted in the case.

The clock was lifted off and dusted down, in a convenient place, and the cords wrapped around the seat board. The head was put on the case again, the weights put in a safe place, and the clock was set in my arms, with the dial toward me, and I was marched off to the shop.

CLEANING AND REPAIRING

Once in the shop there was a standard procedure for taking the clock apart. First the bench was cleaned down and the clock placed upon it.

The bell was then removed and this served as a receptacle for holding small pieces of the clock. A piece of paper was placed in the bottom of the bell to prevent very small articles from passing through the hole.

The escapement was then examined and the pallets removed, after which the back-cock * was put on again to prevent the frames from getting scratched when they were lying on the bench.

Now the clock was turned over on its back and laid on the bench. The hands were taken off, next the dial, and finally the seat board.

Then the dial work and the repeating work were examined and

---

* Back-cock. The brass bracket, attached by two screws to the back plate, from which the pendulum is hung by means of a spring carried between two jaws.

all pins taken out. When this had been done all loose parts were re-moved and the front frame taken off. The wheels inside the frame were exposed and lifted out and the scape wheel put in a safe place. The cords were disengaged from the barrels and put in a coil.

Each part of the clock was cleaned and not a spot of rust or dirt was tolerated. Holes were cleaned in a peculiar manner. A piece of soft wood, like a peg, was pressed into each hole and turned around. Then the wood was removed and scraped—the operation was repeated until the brass did not alter the color of the wood in the slightest degree.

Let us suppose that we have followed these instructions closely and now have our clock apart and cleaned. What damage may we ex-pect to find and what will be the best methods of repair and restora-tion?

If the clock is very old it is most likely that the pivots, pivot holes, pinions, and pallets will all be found pretty badly cut and worn.

PINIONS

When the leaves of a pinion * are badly cut there is no use in filing out the marks, because if the pinion was right in the first place, filing will make the leaves too thin. It is much better to shift the action of the wheels fitting into the pinion.

Sometimes it happens that a leaf is broken out of a pinion. This is a serious matter where it is desired to save the old pinion. In clocks where small pinions of seven and eight leaves are used, there is no way of saving the old pinion except by fastening two rings near the pinion head and to these fastening a new leaf to take the place of the broken one.

WHEELS

Even in very old clocks we seldom see much wear on the teeth of the wheels if the depths were right when the clock was new. Sometimes a tooth, or a few teeth, have been broken by accident. These can easily be replaced in most instances.

---

* Pinion. The smaller of two toothed wheels which are geared into each other. The larger is called a "wheel." The teeth of pinions are known as "leaves."

When teeth have to be replaced, the most desirable method is to dovetail a piece of brass into the rim of the wheel and fasten it with a soft solder that will flow at a moderate heat. This is much better than riveting, because there is always danger of stretching the wheel and putting it out of round.

Sometimes, when teeth are broken, small holes are drilled into the edge of the wheel and pins driven in to take the place of teeth. This method must be looked upon as a temporary measure and is not to be recommended.

PIVOTS

Pivots * may be worn and cut, but it will seldom be found necessary to install new ones, because as a general rule the original pivots were all made thick enough to allow them to be reduced and polished when worn.

But if a new pivot is necessary, either from the effects of wear or from being broken accidentally, there are no arbors in the clock which will not admit a new pivot being inserted.

PIVOT HOLES

When pivot holes are worn, attempts should never be made to close them with punches. The frames are usually so thick that a solid "hole" cannot be made all the way through if they are punched. In some old clocks attempts have been made to close pivot holes by making deep marks with a center punch all the way round. This is "botching" of the worst sort.

If pivot holes are so wide that a smaller one is necessary, the proper procedure is to insert a new bush. The bush should be made eccentric so that it may be turned around into a position that will make the depth between the wheel and pinion most accurate.

ESCAPEMENT

In repairing the escapement, † in some instances there will be difficulty in retaining old parts.

---

* Pivots. The ends of axles, or arbors, that rest in supports.

† Escapement. That part of the clock movement which controls the rate of running.

PALLETS

The pallets * will surely be badly cut; they are the first part of the clock to show wear. Still, in most instances, they can be repaired if judiciously managed.

First the pallets are softened if they were previously hardened. The marks worn in them are then filed out.

Then the pallets are closed by bending them until they closely embrace the number of teeth they originally did. This is best done by placing them in the jaws of a vise and closing the vise very gently. This method is far better than the use of a hammer.

If the workman is not thoroughly conversant with the precise shape these pallets should have, his safest course is to note carefully and preserve the shape of the faces before the pallets are bent.

THE STRIKING PART OF THE CLOCK

The time part of the clock having been repaired, it will now be necessary to look at the striking part. This will probably be found to be out of order.

The method of lifting the hammer is important and the action of the hammer spring is seldom right.

If there are two springs, one to force the hammer down after the clock has raised it up and another shorter one, fastened on the pillar to act as a counter spring, there seldom will be any difficulty in repairs. The only operation necessary is to file out worn parts, polish the acting parts, set the springs a little stronger, and the work is done.

If, however, one spring does the duty of the above two, then the task is more difficult. The part of the hammer stem upon which this spring acts should never be filed beyond the center of the arbor, because in such case the hammer spring has a sliding motion when in action and some of its force is lost.

The point of the spring should be made to work as near the center of the arbor as is possible and the flat end of the spring should be at right angles to the frame.

---

* Pallets. That portion of the escapement which transmits the impulse to the pendulum.

The part of the hammer stem that strikes against the flat end of the spring should be formed with a peculiar curve that will stop the hammer in a particular position and prevent its jarring the bell.

THE REPEATING WORK

This is the part of the mechanism that regulates the number of blows to be struck upon the bell. This mechanism may be found in disorder and worn. The teeth of the rack may require dressing up.

THE COLLET

The collet * in front of the hands is a little thing, but seldom is one seen that is right: one that will hold the hands firm and which will allow them to be moved over small portions of space with ease and certainty. A properly made collet will last as long as the clock.

It is important that the following directions be followed:

Before making a collet, first straighten the minute spring, put it in its place on the center pinion, and put the minute wheel in place on top of it, then put the minute hand in place. The space, or distance, from the surface of the hand to the pin hole in the center pinion is now apparent.

Make the collet just so high that it will just cover this hole, and then cut a slit in the collet just as deep as the hole is wide; make the slit correspond with the hole in every way and in such a manner that when the pin is put in it will fit without any "shake." If the collet is made in this fashion and the minute spring is set up, the hands will always be firm and at the same time move easily and not affect the motion of the clock when they are set forward or backward.

THE PENDULUM

The suspension of the pendulum, the pendulum spring, and the action of the crutch, or back fork, on the pendulum, are all of vital importance. The spring should be perfectly straight and should fit into the slit of the back-cock without shake. The slit should be perfectly straight and at right angles to the frames of the clock.

The back fork should fit easily and without shake. The pendulum

* Collet. In general a collar or band of metal.

bob should swing precisely in a plane with the frames of the clock.

After a clock has been set up in its case and before the head is put on, it is well to get up high enough to look down and see that all these parts work as described above.

RESTORATION OF DIALS AND BRASS WORK ON CASES

The restoration of the dials and brass work should not be attempted by the inexperienced. If the dial is of brass the old lacquer is first removed by boiling the dial in potash. Then the brass is dipped in dilute nitric acid to bring back the original color. After being thoroughly rinsed in rain water and dried, the dial is relacquered.

If the dial has been silvered it is not difficult for an experienced man to resilver it. A great amount of dexterity and judgment is necessary to accomplish this process.

The old workmen used nitrate of silver (lunar caustic) dissolved in rain water to which they added common salt; this gave them a thick curd of silver chloride. They added more salt and cream of tartar, making a paste.

The surface to be silvered was thoroughly washed with a stiff brush and soap. The engraving was then filled with hot sealing wax, after which the dial was rubbed down with pumice stone. After washing and cleaning, the surface was rubbed down with common salt. Then the silver chloride paste was rubbed on. The brass assumed a grayish, streaked appearance and the whole was rubbed with a cream of tartar paste until all was evenly whitened. It was then rinsed in hot water. After this it was heated over a spirit lamp until the sealing wax glistened without melting, at which point a thin coat of spirit varnish was applied.

In the matter of painted dials, restoration is, of course, the work of an artist. It will seldom be necessary to repaint a dial entirely, and it is to be avoided. The old dial should be restored with as little retouching as possible.

Clock, probably by Duffield, owned by Benjamin Franklin.

8

APPRAISING

THE appraisal values of Pennsylvania clocks are of great interest to owners, dealers, and prospective purchasers. One can readily understand the interest of dealers and buyers, but it must be remembered that today an owner is often called upon to set a value on his clock for estate, tax, and insurance purposes.

Certain factors in the appraisal of Pennsylvania clocks are individual and should be understood. For the necessary information we can go to no better source than Mr. John J. Bowman, of Lancaster, Pennsylvania, who speaks with the assurance of more than half a century of experience and observation.

Many years ago he outlined certain rules by which collectors, owners of single clocks, and dealers might base values upon something authoritative and get away from mere guesswork.

Guesswork has, in the past, brought about situations bordering upon the tragic. Mr. Bowman tells of a pathetic incident that came to his attention. A lady who urgently needed money missed an opportunity to sell her clock at a very good price simply because she was told it was worth ten times as much as was offered. She said she would hold it for the higher figure. As Mr. Bowman laconically remarked later, "She will find that 'holding' is the right word."

Three principal factors affect the value of a Pennsylvania clock: (a) age; (b) the intrinsic merit of the clock and case, and (c) the name of the maker. These three factors should be considered together rather than separately.

Only the very oldest clocks are valuable for age alone. Now, if a clock has great age, a movement of superior technical design and workmanship, a case of fine wood and workmanship and architectural beauty—then the clock is of great value. The more recently a clock has been made the more it must have of intrinsic merit in works and case to give it value. Certain makers' clocks are more valued than others and this is simply because their clocks show design and workmanship finer than the average.

To judge the rarity and value of a certain clock we must depend upon: (a) a general knowledge of the history of clockmaking in Pennsylvania; (b) a knowledge of periods and types, and (c) records of individual makers.

Let us briefly review the history of clockmaking in Pennsylvania and its bearing upon values.

Between 1682 and 1750, clocks were found only in the homes of the wealthier colonists. Clocks were imported from England and the few Pennsylvania makers were largely confined to Philadelphia and possibly the adjacent counties of Bucks and Chester. So rare are clocks of this period that they require individual study for appraisal. It may be stated, however, that these clocks are now very rare.

By 1750 the increasing wealth of the colonists brought about an increasing demand for clocks. This was met by clockmakers who pushed westward after serving an apprenticeship in Philadelphia and also by European clockmakers who came to Pennsylvania. Although there were a good many clockmakers, clocks were still only for the comparatively wealthy.

The growth in Pennsylvania clockmaking steadily went forward until it was halted by the Revolution in 1775. Money became scarce and many clockmakers turned to gunsmithing and like industries.

Some very fine clocks—now of great value—were made in the period starting about 1750 and ending with the Revolution. The clocks remaining today from this period are by no means numerous, yet we may safely state that this was the golden era of Pennsylvania clock-making, represented by David Rittenhouse, Edward Duffield, John Wood (Jr.), and others. Cases often represent the Colonial cabinet-maker at his best.

By about 1800, prosperity returned and the handmade tall case Pennsylvania clock enjoyed a great revival. Clockmakers plied their craft throughout the State and there were few communities of any consequence that did not have two or three. Farmers became prosperous and had clocks made for their homes.

The revival continued until about 1830, when the New England shelf clock, costing only a fifth as much as a handmade tall case clock, appeared in Pennsylvania. We may feel perfectly safe in saying that by 1850 the era of the Pennsylvania tall case clock had passed. Tall case clocks made in Pennsylvania after 1850 rarely have anything of interest to make them valuable to the collector.

Therefore, in judging the average Pennsylvania clock that may be offered for sale we may say that—in the absence of records concerning its maker—the greatest likelihood is that it was made between 1800 and 1830.

It is well to remember two characteristics generally indicating that a clock was made before the Revolution: a metal dial ornamented in relief or by engraving, or both; and sometimes wheel work so designed that the clock must be wound every day. The vogue for painted or enameled dials began after 1800.

It is peculiar to Pennsylvania clocks that they are often found at sales. Usually the prices of clocks at auction are taken as a criterion, but several unusual factors are found in Pennsylvania. One factor is the great sentimental value placed on the clocks by descendants of original owners. Mr. Bowman tells of a sale at which the auctioneer knew that the wealthy grandson of an original owner was bidding for the clock that once belonged to his grandfather. The price was run up well above $1,000. Owners of other clocks by the same maker then thought that their clocks were also worth this price. But actually the high bid represented a sentimental value for a particular item only.

Prices at auctions are also dependent upon the general prosperity prevailing at the time of the sale—prices are higher during boom times than during depressions. The number and kind of persons at a sale also have much to do with prices realized. If dealers are doing the bidding, prices will not go as high as when several collectors are present. On the other hand, collectors are often hard bidders.

Basically there is no absolute market value for an old Pennsylvania clock as there is for wheat, coal, or other essential commodities, yet over the years certain values have been established which may be regarded as minimums.

As a basis let us take the long-range prices realized in many sales over a period of years for Pennsylvania clocks of average merit, clocks made between 1800 and 1830, since these are the ones which usually appear in sales. They will be of the eight-day type, with enameled or painted dials. The cases will represent local cabinet work of varying degrees of distinction. The clock will be in fairly good condition, needing few repairs and little restoration. Such a clock has a minimum value of about $200 and it will range up to about $500. Exceptionally fine specimens will bring up to $1,000.

Now let us turn to the clocks of David Rittenhouse. Here we find the Pennsylvania clock at its best. It would be safe to state that any David Rittenhouse eight-day clock would command a price of $2,000 to $2,500. It must be understood that we are here talking about authentic David Rittenhouse clocks—clocks that have not been tampered with. The value of some Rittenhouse clocks may well go up above $10,000 for choice specimens with a history.

An Edward Duffield clock would bring at least $1,000 since the man is well known for his excellent work, and excellent clockwork is almost always housed in fine cases. A John Wood clock has a minimum value of about $600 and from that minimum the price may rise to $2,000 for extremely fine specimens.

Where a case has been made by a now-famous Colonial cabinet-maker it is not unusual for the price of the clock to be correspondingly very high.

There are Pennsylvania clocks to fit every purse, and of course we should consider that they all rise steadily in value from year to year. If it is bought at a reasonable price, there is probably no better investment than a Pennsylvania clock.

The public are respectfully informed that Bells of every description can be had at all times for Churches, Court-houses, Factories, Steamboats, Corporations, Companies, and all other persons, having use for Bells will please call at the Foundry, where they will find the best assortment in the United States. A large stock constantly on hand.

J. WILBANK,

No. 262, Market Street, Philadelphia.

9

PENNSYLVANIA-GERMAN FOLK ART AND THE PENNSYLVANIA CLOCK

Fraktur Schriften, the illuminated writings of the Pennsylvania Germans, are unique in the annals of folk art. The medieval art of illuminating manuscripts survived in Pennsylvania until very recent times, and the effects of this art can still be seen. As late as 1840 the Pennsylvania Germans were pursuing an art in their homes that had its origin in the Western World in the seventh-century monasteries of Ireland.

"Illuminated writings" is a term applied to hand-colored manuscripts in which the text is embellished by the ornamentation of the initial letter or word with gold, silver, or color, and this decoration may extend to miniature designs on the margin of the page.

Fraktur is a German word and refers to a certain type of design in Gothic letters. This word gave its name to the *Fraktur Schriften* (*Fraktur* writings) of the Pennsylvania Germans.

The art of illuminating manuscripts was carried from the monasteries of Ireland to the Scottish coast and England by early missionaries. St. Boniface (680–754) took a richly illuminated Gospel with him to Germany and thus introduced the art on the Continent.

In early days the art was almost exclusively confined to monks. The invention of printing (1455) and the Reformation during the sixteenth century had much to do with the decline of the art in the monasteries of Europe, but it lived on among the people of Germany. There are still extant some now very rare little books explaining the mixing of colors and other techniques. These books were for the people and not for the monks who had previously been masters of the art.

Our next step is to trace the passage of the art to Pennsylvania. The first Germans came to Pennsylvania in 1683 and the migration steadily increased until it reached its height between 1730 and 1750, although it continued until the Revolution. These Germans brought the art to their new homes; it was a part of them. The art in Pennsylvania reached its best expression between 1790 and 1840 in the generations following the pioneers. It was lavished upon manuscripts of daily life such as baptismal and marriage certificates, house blessings and book plates.

The Pennsylvania German's love of color was innate. He used it in decorating the everyday things of life, and his gardens were bright with color. He painted his barns red, but his artistic sense rebelled at leaving the side of a building a mass of red; so he added designs and markings. Chests were decorated in color.

While the design and color of the *Fraktur Schriften* had a great effect upon the decoration of barns, chests, and other things, there was a distinction. The manuscripts were pure folk art, an art practiced by the people themselves and expressing the individuality of the respective artists. The barns, chests, and furniture were decorated by "professionals," as it were, and rarely by the people in general. Immediately after the designs and techniques pass into the hands of "professionals," an art ceases to be a true folk art.

Thus the well-known markings on Pennsylvania German barns cannot be regarded as pure folk art. These were executed by "professionals," even though the artist might be only an itinerant painter. There still exist price lists showing the fees charged for painting various designs on barns. The situation regarding the decoration of chests and other household items was much the same.

However, the same basic designs may be found both on the *Frak-*

tur Schriften and on barns, chests, and other objects. The manuscripts represent the true folk art of the people; the barns and other decorations represent the reflection of this art.

Now, among the *Fraktur Schriften* may be found some so-called "clock *Frakturs*." These have a clock for the central design. The clock is surrounded by various sayings having to do with each hour of the day. These clock *Frakturs* show the importance attached to clocks and time by these Pennsylvania Germans and are true folk art. The Schwenkfelder Library, in Pennsburg, Pennsylvania, possesses a comprehensive collection of clock *Frakturs*.

Despite his love of color, the Pennsylvania German seldom, if ever, painted or decorated his clock cases. There was a beauty in the woods used to make cases that appealed to the artistic sense of the Pennsylvania German, a beauty which he was reluctant to cover with paint. Walnut, the fruit woods, and later mahogany all appealed to him. So great was this interest that small boys made collections of blocks of wood which they polished and identified.

The decoration of clock dials, however, was another matter, and here the influence of the *Fraktur Schriften* may be seen. This is an influence that has not been stressed before. The decorations on the dial of a Pennsylvania German clock are distinctive and set it apart from the painted dials of New and Old England.

Clock dials of the painted variety, in common use after the Revolution, were usually bought from dealers and were not made by the clockmakers themselves. Although these dials were bought, the local artist was often called upon to add decorations. This was the period when the painted dial took the place of the brass dial and also the period (1790 to 1840) that marked the golden age of *Fraktur Schriften*.

The late Henry S. Borneman, authority on *Fraktur Schriften* who owned the outstanding collection of these items, would tell how a clock made for his father came into being. The works were ordered from a local clockmaker. At the same time a large piece of mahogany was selected and purchased. From the latter the cabinetmaker cut the boards and made the case.

The dial for this clock, a white-enameled one, was purchased. It was equipped with the moon device. A woman who was a local artist of some note was commissioned to paint scenes upon the moon wheel.

"What is the 'something' which distinguishes a Pennsylvania German dial from other dials?" is a fair question. An examination of *Fraktur Schriften* will soon disclose that "something." The same designs, details, forms, and colorings are used.

While it cannot be denied that there is a symbolism in the folk art of the Pennsylvania German, it is, however, an obvious symbolism and not an attempt to be obscure or occult. Flowers were often used, but flowers with which the artist and those who admired his work were familiar. Great efforts have been made to read into the tulip design, so often met with, an Oriental influence. But the truth is that the tulip was a familiar flower that lent itself to pleasing and colorful design.

Birds frequently appeared in the compositions. Again they offered a wide latitude of form and color. The turtle dove, for instance, was regarded as a symbol of love and beauty.

Stars were used, and it has been said that the five-pointed star indicated personality, that the six-pointed star of David was a symbol of the Old Testament, that the seven-pointed star represented the soul. Whatever truth there may be in this, the star and circle did present a challenge in pleasing geometric design.

The influence of *Fraktur Schriften* upon the decoration of the dials of the clocks of Pennsylvania Germans is a subject that offers a new field of study and appreciation. A study of clock dial painting in this light will further enhance the pleasure of owning a Pennsylvania clock, and will open the door to an appreciation of those manuscripts which represent a true folk art going back some thirteen hundred years.

10

GRANDFATHER'S CLOCK

IT was a song writer, Henry Clay Work, not a clockmaker, who gave the tall case clock the name by which it is now almost universally known, "grandfather's clock." Since this was not until 1875, none of the men who actually made the clocks ever knew them by that name.

But Work did far more than give the clocks a name. His two songs, "Grandfather's Clock" and the now little-known "Sequel to Grandfather's Clock"—together with the revival of interest in American history brought about by the Centennial Exhibition in Philadelphia in 1876—did much to save the old timepieces from oblivion.

It has been said that "the true feelings of a people speak through the songs they sing." Since 800,000 copies of "Grandfather's Clock" were soon sold, it may be said that the song reflected the feelings of America toward the tall clocks of its "grandfathers."

The dictionaries of today recognize "grandfather's clock," or "grandfather clock," as the name for "the weight-and-pendulum eight-day clock in a tall case formerly in common use." It might, therefore, be well to ascertain the date of Work's "Grandfather's Clock" and answer the question, "When was the clock of the song made?"

The clock in the song was bought when "grandfather" was born and "stopped short" after 90 years when the old man died. Work wrote his song "several years" before it was published in 1875. "Grandfather's clock," therefore was made about 1780.

The clock shown on the cover of the song sheet, however, is not a "grandfather's clock" but rather resembles a "regulator" of about 1850. The moon was crudely added by some forgotten artist.

Henry Clay Work was born in Middletown, Conn., in 1832. In 1854 he was in Chicago working as a printer when he began his successful career as a song writer.

After the Chicago fire, in 1871, Work came east, living for a time in Philadelphia and later in nearby Vineland, New Jersey. "Grandfather's Clock" was undoubtedly written during the Philadelphia period. It was published in 1875, but we have the author's word for it that it was written some time before.

It is not surprising that Work saw in the "grandfather's clock" a living thing that was part of the old man's life. The sentiment had often been expressed before.

I love to contemplate an old clock [wrote John F. Watson, the Philadelphia annalist, in 1830], one of those relics of bygone times that come down to us wrapped in veneration, telling their tale of simple yet touching interest.

How erect and prim it stands in the corner, like some faded specimen of maiden antiquity. Its face bears the mark of beauty—of beauty decayed but not obliterated. It is plain that it has seen its best days, but it is equally evident that it was the pride and ornament of its day.

Years have gone by since the ancient monitor of time first started on its course, and now they who started out with it in the morning of life, where are they, aye, where are they? But the old clock ticks blithely and patiently as ever. The voices and footsteps are silent of those who journeyed up with it to a good old age. A new race succeeds and stands before it, as they watch its progress their hours are also passing. Mark the impressive lesson from the old clock.

Work was not the first to write a song about an old clock. In 1856

J. A. Fowler's "Oh! the Old, Old, Clock" appeared. Fowler wrote, "Its hands tho' old, had a touch of gold." And the "tick! tick! tick!" of the long seconds pendulum was imitated in the music.

But Work had a serious purpose in writing his songs—in melody and verse he pictured and recorded the life of America as it was moving from the last pioneer days into a great industrial era. It was fitting that this man should tell the story of the old clocks.

The "Sequel to Grandfather's Clock," published in 1878, was advertised as illustrating the final fate of the old timekeeper. Here the picture on the cover is really a "grandfather's clock" and the scene vividly depicts the old clock being taken away by "Ezekiel Slater— Yankee Clocks."

Work was quite adept at rhythm. In the "Sequel to Grandfather's Clock" he imitates the Yankee clock, "the stuck up thing on the wall," with its rapid "tick-tock" of a short pendulum, while in "Grandfather's Clock" he imitates the stately and dignified "tick, tick, tick,"—"in exact time"—of the long seconds pendulum.

The term "grandmother's clock" is today heard in speech and seen in print—although it has not yet reached the dictionaries.

It was almost inevitable that the success of Work's "Grandfather's Clock" would be followed by another song, "Grandmother's Clock." In 1878 there appeared "free" with the "New York Family Story Paper" the song and chorus—"Grandmother's Clock." On the cover the words are credited to Jno. F. Cowan, while on the song itself they are credited to Alice Dale. The music is by Geo. W. Morgan. The song, "in regular time, like the pendulum of a clock," is of little importance today, but the name "grandmother's clock" was created.

What is known today as a "grandmother's clock" is really a "dwarf" or miniature tall clock. Some have fixed the height at from forty to fifty inches.

An old newspaper clipping, unfortunately not dated, describes the "grandmother's clock":

There is now what is referred to as a grandmother's clock. Modeled on smaller lines than the ordinary grandfather, but similar in construction, this clock stands five feet high and is much in demand by housewives and it does not cost as much as a grandfather.

11

WATCHES, WATCHMAKERS, AND WATCHPAPERS OF PENNSYLVANIA

WE have seen that in 1683, when Philadelphia was only one year old and a struggling little town of five hundred inhabitants, William Carter was working as a watchmaker and repairman. Watches were important in Philadelphia and Pennsylvania from the beginning and increased in importance with the growth of a prosperous merchant and mariner class.

The watch itself may be said to have had its beginning in about 1500, when Peter Henlein, a locksmith of Nuremberg, Germany, utilized the main spring. He is credited with having first used a tightly coiled ribbon of steel as the driving power for a timepiece, thus making the portable clock, and the watch, possible.

It is not within the province of this book to trace the early history of watches and watchmaking in continental Europe and England, or even to mention many of the great names involved in inventions and improvements. We need only recall that by 1682, when Pennsylvania was founded, the watch had reached a high degree of development.

Thomas Tompion (1639–1713), "the father of English watchmaking," was at the height of his career.

Since it was not until after 1850 that the factory-made watch took hold in America, the period covered by this book—1682 to 1850—embraces the individually handmade watches of the past. As might be expected, the watches found in Philadelphia and Pennsylvania in the early eighteenth century were largely of English origin.

Undoubtedly the Quaker influence had much to do with keeping watches within utilitarian bounds, no matter how wealthy the owner might be. As late as 1800 there were Friends who expressed concern about the habit of young men showing gold watch chains in public.

Fortunately we have a description of the "average" watch carried by a well-to-do citizen of Philadelphia in 1738. In that year, John Webb, a friend of Franklin, advertised for a watch that had been stolen from him. It was a silver watch with an outside case of fishskin studded and hooped with silver. Gold watches were rare in Philadelphia in those times, and the chains were usually of steel or silver rather than gold.

In these early days there were men in Philadelphia who sold watches, but the movements were usually imported from England and later from France. Even if the watch carried the signature of a Philadelphia watchmaker, the parts were imported. If the movement alone was imported, there is a possibility that the case was made in Philadelphia. But it must be remembered that whether the watchmaker made the case or not he usually put his name on the movement. For this reason great care must be exercised in studying a Philadelphia watch of an early vintage.

Watches, like clocks, have an enhanced value if their full histories are known. For instance, there is extant a watch which Edward Duffield "made" for Franklin. The value of this watch lies largely in the fact that it belonged to Franklin rather than that it was "made" by Duffield.

Therefore, in appraising a Philadelphia or Pennsylvania watch it seems that we are on the safe side in saying that the value depends upon who originally owned it, rather than upon who "made" it. A watch that belonged to an ancestor is proof of the family's importance in the past.

Watson, the annalist of Philadelphia, tells us that it was the custom of General Washington while residing in the City as President of the United States to go every day at noon to set his watch by Clark's standard time at the southeast corner of Front and High Streets. The president lived in a mansion on High Street between Fifth and Sixth. When Washington arrived at Clark's, all the porters took off their hats and stood uncovered until he had adjusted his watch. Washington always bowed to such salutations and lifted his hat in return.

The watch in Philadelphia, probably more than in any other American city, was a symbol of financial security and the mark of a dependable man. This feeling persisted into the nineteenth century.

In the 1830s, when the factory system of England was taking hold in the mills of New England and there was great agitation in some quarters regarding the condition of the workers—a Philadelphia physician and maker of medicines established a model village and glass manufactory.

Dr. T. W. Dyott founded Dyottville in Philadelphia County. The venture stands out as an experiment in early American enterprise. He carefully trained his apprentices in glass blowing and in citizenship, since he believed, "with the great Lord Bacon," that "the Wealth of a State consisted in the Virtue of its Citizens."

In a very rare little pamphlet published in 1833, Dr. Dyott outlined his plans. Among other things it was possible for an apprentice to earn additional money by increasing production. This sum was kept intact for the apprentice so that he might have a small capital with which to begin life. It could be drawn on for only two purposes—the purchase of fine clothes for Sundays and for a watch. The good doctor looked upon a watch as a necessity for an up-and-coming young man.

While the clockmaker, in early America, was usually also a watchmaker, the watch was so important in Philadelphia—and the wealth of the place was such—that not a few found it profitable to devote their attention exclusively to watches. They not only made watches, but imported movements and parts. Careful fitting and fine adjustments were required. Many of these men, and some women who were in the trade, were not clockmakers.

Philadelphia, in Colonial times, was a cosmopolitan city and from about 1750 to the Revolution was the political and commercial center of the Colonies. We have seen that many Germans came to Philadelphia and Pennsylvania and among these were many clock- and watchmakers. Later, a number of French came, and an attempt was made to start a French-language newspaper. As one looks through the list * of Philadelphia craftsmen, therefore, many will appear who were watchmakers alone. Some of the great family names of watchmakers of France appear in the Philadelphia list.

LANCASTER, PA., AND WATCHES

The city of Lancaster was founded in 1730 by Andrew Hamilton and his son James upon ground granted to the father by the sons of William Penn. Situated in a rich farming country, Lancaster prospered. It was not long before it attracted some fine clockmakers and became a center of the industry. Many tall case clocks were made, and apprentices trained under the Lancaster masters went far and wide to establish themselves in the south and west.

Today Lancaster is known throughout the world as a center of watchmaking. This distinction is due to one large company, the Hamilton Watch Company, named in honor of Andrew Hamilton. Much as one would like to build up a continuity by having the clockmakers of Lancaster turn to watchmaking when the Connecticut shelf clock took the place of the tall case clock in the period between 1840 and 1850, this cannot be done. There is little personal connection between the clockmakers of Lancaster and the great watchmaking industry that grew up some twenty-five years after the tall case clock industry ceased. But it can be said that the old clockmakers had created an atmosphere of horology for watchmaking that was to follow.

The American watchmaking industry on a large scale began in a factory in Roxbury, Massachusetts, in 1850. This factory was moved to Waltham, Massachusetts, four years later. Immediately prior to this,

---

* See page 168ff.

England and Switzerland had been sending watches to the United States in large quantities. The present American watch industry is the outgrowth and survival of more than sixty different companies that were formed over a period of years.

In the days following the War between the States, many self-reliant men built railroads and factories beyond the frontiers. One such man was John C. Adams, who devoted his life to organizing watch companies. So energetic was he that he was known as "The Great American Starter." He lived in Chicago but was convinced that the success of the Waltham company could be duplicated eslewhere.

Adams not only sold enough stock in Chicago to build and equip a watch factory at Elgin, Illinois, but went to the Waltham plant and convinced a group of technical men to come to Elgin. This company was a success from its start in 1867 and is today probably the largest factory in the world making jeweled watches. During his lifetime, Adams promoted six watch companies in the United States from Pennsylvania to California.

Early in the 1870s Adams appeared in Lancaster and persuaded some of the citizens of the town to subscribe $78,000 toward a capitalization of $100,000 to start a watch factory. The Adams and Perry Watch Manufacturing Co. was duly organized in 1874. A new factory building was completed in 1875. The model for the first watch, and most of the machinery for producing it, were ready by April of the following year. The product was a very good watch, but scarcity of working capital forced the company into bankruptcy in June 1876.

The factory was idle for a year, during which time many efforts were made to reorganize the company. A new corporation, The Lancaster, Pa., Watch Company, was formed and the factory started again in September 1877. Financial difficulties still hounded the project, and in October 1878 a new corporation, The Lancaster, Pa., Watch Company, Limited, became the owner.

In May 1879 still another company, The Lancaster Watch Company, took over the factory. Then, in 1883, after the factory had been closed for some time, another company was formed using the same name. Finally one of the original stockholders, Abram Bitner, bought all outstanding stock and became practically sole owner in 1884.

In 1886 an entirely new company, The Keystone Standard Watch Co., was organized by some men of means in Lancaster. This company had a paid-in capital of a half million dollars. The group bought the real estate and machinery of the previous company, lowered the quality of the watches, and introduced methods of marketing that created hostility toward Lancaster watches in the trade. The company went into bankruptcy in 1890 and its assets were sold by the sheriff to another group of Lancaster citizens who that year had bought the assets of the Aurora Watch Company, of Aurora, Illinois; this Aurora company had also fallen into financial difficulties.

This latter group of citizens set about creating a watch company that would be a credit and an asset to Lancaster. They took what was left of the Keystone Standard Watch Co. and the Aurora Watch Company, met in October 1892, and organized the Hamilton Watch Company.

An addition was built to the old Keystone plant and the best of its machinery combined with the best of the Aurora plant. A new watch of great accuracy was designed. This watch immediately became popular with railroad men, largely because of the then recently adopted watch-inspection rules of the railroads. The Hamilton watch became known as "The Railroad Timekeeper of America" and played a major role in the drama of American railroading.

The story of the watchmaking industry in Lancaster is an important one in the annals of American enterprise. There was a persistence and courage in the face of financial disaster that must be admired.

EZRA F. BOWMAN OF LANCASTER

No story of horology in Pennsylvania, or the United States, would be complete without mention of Ezra F. Bowman, descendant of one of the pioneer families of Lancaster County. As early as 1867 this man's father "previsioned the modern use of schools for vocational training." The apprentice system for training craftsmen was extremely wasteful: of the seven years served, only about two could be credited to actual instruction. He reasoned that it was far more economical to pay a thousand dollars for the two years' instruction and living, and thus gain five years of earning ability as a journeyman.

Accordingly the elder Bowman contracted with a European master watchmaker to teach his son on a plan he had conceived.

Under this system Ezra F. Bowman became a master watchmaker. He found employment in the Adams and Perry Company, but after that concern went into receivership he opened his own retail watch and clock business in 1877. Two years later, in 1879, he began to manufacture the Bowman watch, his motive being to demonstrate that as fine a watch could be made in America as abroad. The watch proved this contention, but he soon found that it cost more to make the watch than it could be sold for. He sold the watch manufacturing plant to J. C. Stevens, of Atlanta, Georgia, in 1882.

In 1887 he founded the Bowman Technical School for training young men in the crafts of clock- and watchmaking. This school put into practice a plan of vocational education that made the old apprentice system obsolete. Ezra F. Bowman died in 1901.

WATCHPAPERS

In recent years there has been increasing interest in the study and collecting of watchpapers. Watchpapers are probably best defined and understood from a short account of their origin and development.

Early watches had an inner and outer case, and before the middle of the 18th century it became the custom to place a small circular piece of either fabric or paper between these cases. This acted as a cushion to keep the outer case more firmly closed and to protect the works of the watch from dust. The circular piece of fabric was embellished by the needlework of young women and became a sentimental token to be given to a friend or relative.

The watchmakers soon saw that these small discs might be used to their advantage. While the discs provided a protective padding for the watch and in addition to this had a sentimental value, it became obvious that they could be used as a means of advertising. The custom arose of watchmakers inserting their own papers to advertise their businesses, whenever watches were repaired or cleaned. Watchpapers carried the name and location of the shop of the watchmaker, and sometimes carried elaborate illustrations or designs. These watchpapers were

Watchpapers: actual size. (*From the Collection of Ernest A. Cramer.*)

engraved, lithographed, and printed and their use continued until the 1870s.

It was not uncommon for the watchmaker to write the date of the repairs, and even the price, on the back of the paper inserted in a watch. Often as many as five or six watchpapers, advertising different craftsmen, will be found in one old watch.

The diameters of watchpapers vary from one and one-half inch to as much as two and one-half inches; the average will be found to be about two inches. Some watchpapers were engraved by rather well known artists, while others were crude. Yet all have an interest.

There are rare and valuable collections of watchpapers in the Historical Society of Pennsylvania, Philadelphia, and in the Chester County Historical Society, West Chester, Pennsylvania. The largest and most comprehensive collection, however, is in the American Antiquarian Society, Worcester, Massachusetts. This collection is rich in Philadelphia and Pennsylvania items. Mrs. Dorothea E. Spear, of the American Antiquarian Society, has made a detailed study of the subject and may be regarded as the outstanding authority.

12

CLOCKS AND BELLS OF
THE STATE HOUSE

"And ye shall hallow the fiftieth year, and proclaim liberty throughout all the land unto all the inhabitants thereof: it shall be a jubilee unto you: and ye shall return every man unto his possession and ye shall return every man unto his family" (Leviticus, 25:10).

THE clocks and bells of the State House in Philadelphia are as deeply entrenched in the history and traditions of the nation as the building itself. They are enduring memorials, standing for integrity and independence.

The architect of the main building was Andrew Hamilton. This man, who died in 1741, has been called "the day-star of the American Revolution." In 1735 he defended John Peter Zenger, publisher of the *New York Weekly Journal*, and established the freedom of the press on American soil.

Between 1682 and 1729 the Assembly of the Province of Pennsylvania was without a fixed place of meeting, and its sessions were held in various places, including the Quaker meeting houses and the Court House at Second and Market Streets.

In 1729 money was appropriated for the purchase of ground for a state house. Andrew Hamilton was speaker of the Assembly and chairman of the committee in charge.

The building was commenced in 1732 and was ready for use, though not finished, in October 1735, when the Assembly first sat in it. In 1741 it was considered completed. The tower and steeple were not then built, and for nine years no effort was made to add to the main structure.

In 1750 the Assembly authorized the erection of a building on "the south side of the State-House, to contain a staircase, with a suitable place for hanging a bell." A wooden steeple was erected upon this tower.

In the latter part of 1751, Isaac Norris, speaker of the Assembly at that time, authorized the Colonial agent in London, Robert Charles, to procure a bell of about two thousand pounds' weight,

with the following words well shaped in large letters round it, viz:—
By order of the Assembly of the Province of Pennsylvania, for the State House in the city of Philadelphia, 1752.
And underneath,
Proclaim Liberty through all the land to all the inhabitants thereof.—
Levit. xxv.10

This bell duly arrived but "was cracked by a stroke of the clapper without any other violence." Since the ship captain who brought it from England could not take it on board his ship for return, two workmen, Pass and Stow, undertook to recast it. This they did and the American bell was hung in its place early in 1753.

There was dissatisfaction regarding the bell, and Pass and Stow asked permission again to recast it. In June 1753 the second essay of the American bell was placed in position. This was destined to become the now famous Liberty Bell.

Meanwhile the English founder was ordered to send over another of his make. This second bell duly arrived and by order of the Assembly both bells were retained.

The State House as it appeared in 1778. This is the most authentic view of the clock and steeple as they appeared about the time of the signing of the Declaration of Independence. The origin of this view is most interesting. Early in July 1778, Chevalier Conrad Alexandre Gérard arrived in Philadelphia as the first foreign minister accredited to the United States. Charles Willson Peale painted a portrait of M. Gérard, and in the background of this portrait was the view of the State House shown. Rembrandt Peale, son of Charles Willson Peale, made an engraving of the view of the State House, taking the detail out of the above portrait. For this reason the engraving shown is often attributed to Charles Willson Peale. When the Gérard portrait was cleaned some years back, the view of the State House was "discovered" and the origin of the view fixed.

The Assembly did not confine its interests to bells. In March 1752 the body determined to have a "large clock which should strike on the Bell in the Tower and have a suitable dial to show the Hours and Minutes."

This clock was ordered in Philadelphia,

for [wrote Isaac Norris] we expect it will prove better than any they would send us from England, where, once they had it put out of their hands, they will have done with it; but here the workman would be made very uneasy if he did not exert his utmost skill, as we do not stint him in the price of his labor.

This clock was made by Thomas Stretch, not by his father Peter Stretch, as it has been erroneously stated. (Peter Stretch died in 1746.) Thomas Stretch was a very prominent man in his time, a founder and the first governor of the famous fishing club, The State in Schuylkill.

In 1759 Thomas Stretch was paid £494/5s/5½d for the clock and its care for six years. He died in 1765, after six years.

The Stretch clock was most unusual. It was not in the steeple. The movement of the clock was in the middle of the main building, immediately under the roof and near the tower. The dials were placed at either end of the building and connected to the movement by means of rods running through pipes.

The dial on the west wall was protected by an ornamental case running down to the ground, in imitation of the tall case clocks of the period. In January 1762 Edward Duffield succeeded Thomas Stretch as custodian of the clock, and he in turn was followed by David Rittenhouse in March 1775.

The stirring events enacted in the State House in 1776 are too well known to require repeating. But it must be remembered that the Declaration of Independence was first read by John Nixon, a member of the Provincial Council of Safety, on Monday, July 8, 1776, from the platform of the observatory that had been erected in the State House yard by the American Philosophical Society. The purpose of this observatory was to study the transit of Venus over the sun which took place June 3, 1768. David Rittenhouse was in charge of this study.

The bell to be later known as the Liberty Bell was taken down in 1777 at the approach of the British and removed to Allentown. When the enemy evacuated the city, it was returned. It was afterwards used only on special occasions. In July 1835 it was badly cracked while being tolled in memory of Chief Justice Marshall who had died in Philadelphia two days before. It was rung after this, but it was so much injured during the celebration of Washington's birthday in 1843 that it was never used again.

The wooden steeple, becoming decayed, was taken down in 1781. The heavy "fraim whereon the Bell used to hang" was lowered into the brick tower and the "Liberty Bell" was again suspended from its beam. Immediately in front of the tower on the main roof, the second bell, or "clock bell," was suspended and a shed built over it.

After the spring of 1799 the chambers hitherto occupied by the National and State Legislatures were vacated. In 1802 Charles Willson Peale obtained permission from the State Legislature to use the building for his museum.

Under an act of Legislature of March 11, 1816, the City of Philadelphia became the actual owner of the property.* Lafayette's visit to the city in 1824 aroused memories of 1776, and a movement was started to restore the building.

The committee in charge of restoration went into great detail regarding the clock. One member stated that "the clock then in use might well last for fifty years." Another member said, "If there is anything proverbial, it is the badness of the clock at the State House. It is an excusing not a regulating clock. It is a clock which affords no rule to go by, but a rule not to go by, for everybody knows it can never go right."

In making an estimate for the restoration the committee stated, "The value of the old clock is left out of view, as from its age and con-

---

* Since January 1, 1951, the Independence Hall group of buildings has been administered by the National Park Service of the United States Department of the Interior as part of the Independence National Historical Park Project. Under the terms of a cooperative agreement made in 1950 between the City of Philadelphia and the Department of the Interior, the National Park Service assumed the administration and maintenance of the buildings and Independence Square, with the City retaining ownership of the property.

dition, it is not considered of more value than old metal, except the dials, which might be used for the new clock, and an allowance made for them by the maker."

The committee was also impressed "with the necessity of having a uniform time for the city, which would be obtained, by having a good clock under the superintendence of a careful person."

The committee reported that it had received a proposal from Isaiah Lukens to make a clock for the city at a cost of $2,000 and from John Wilbank to cast a new 4,000-pound bell for $1,800. Wilbank offered to credit the city with $400 for the old bell.

"A grand raising frolic" to the workmen celebrated the completion of the new steeple July 4, 1828. The new clock, with four faces and this time placed in the steeple or tower, was made by Lukens.

The new Wilbank bell was placed in position in September 1828, but like its predecessor it was short-lived. The founder was required to cast a second bell, which was placed in the tower in December 1828. When the new arrangement whereby the hammer struck the hour by means of the clockwork was tried at 3:00 P.M. on December 30, the whole machinery was found to operate perfectly.

It will be noted that Wilbank never received the "Liberty Bell" or its companion, the "clock bell," when he made the new bell for the Isaiah Lukens clock.

Isaiah Lukens appeared in the Philadelphia directories as "horologist, town clockmaker and mechanist."

As to the subsequent fate of the Stretch clock and the "clock bell," the companion to the Liberty Bell, a little-known story unfolds which is an epic of the enduring principle of freedom of worship in America.

Father Matthew Carr, of the Order of St. Augustine, came to Philadelphia from Dublin in the spring of 1796. The earliest direct evidence of the beginning of St. Augustine's Church on North Fourth Street is a list, dated June 12, 1796, of "subscribers" or contributors for the proposed new building.

Little is known of the history of St. Augustine's Church between the opening of the subscribers' list in 1796 and the actual opening of the church on June 7, 1801.

In 1830 the Stretch clock and bell of the State House were placed in the steeple of St. Augustine's Church "for the convenience of residents of that section of the City." Both clock and bell were held in trust for the City.

Some confusion exists regarding financial arrangements between church and city. There is still extant in the archives of Villanova University a "memorandum of agreement," dated 1835, between the Rev. Michael Hurley, pastor of St. Augustine's Church, and the "Mayor, Aldermen & Citizens of Philadelphia." It was agreed that the

Clock & Bell shall be and remain in the said Church & that the said Pastor and his successors shall have the use of said Bell for religious and other purposes: that the same shall not be rung for fires: the expense of keeping the same in repair to be borne by the party of the Second Part [the City] and no rent shall be charged by the Party of the First Part [the church].

It is indeed difficult today to understand the bigotry and hatred which existed among certain elements in Philadelphia in 1844. These feelings flared into mob violence, which culminated in the burning of two Catholic churches on May 8, 1844—St. Michael's and St. Augustine's. Further destruction was only stopped by the arrival of the military.

The Stretch clock was consumed in the fire and the companion bell to the Liberty Bell crashed into the ruins as the steeple fell.

The fragments of the bell were gathered from the ruins of the church and cast into another bell by Joseph Bernhard, a bell founder who had established himself only two years before at 262 High Street. This man was a skilled craftsman and his firm was still in business in the 1870s.

Despite the troubled times, the Augustinians had laid the foundation for Villanova University "about ten miles from Philadelphia, within a few paces of Lancaster Turnpike and the Columbia Railroad." The institution was first known as St. Thomas of Villanova College. It had been closed for a few years but reopened in 1846. The Bernhard bell became the college bell and was used as such for half a century; then it served as a church bell in Jamaica, Long Island, and finally was returned to Villanova as a cherished relic.

It seems most fitting that this bell now at Villanova—all that is left of the first State House "clock bell" and clock—should stand as symbolic evidence that intolerance cannot survive on American soil.

After Lafayette's visit in 1824 the name Independence Hall was given to the State House by resolution of City Councils.

The Centennial of the nation in 1876 again aroused great interest in the State House. There was a demand for a new clock and a new bell. The nation had expanded and the feeling had grown that Independence Hall was the shrine of the entire United States rather than the possession of a city or state.

The Wilbank bell was taken down in June 1876 and replaced by a 13,000-pound bell, the gift of a citizen, Henry Seybert. This bell was cast by Meneely & Kimberly, of Troy, New York. Around the top was cast, "Glory to God in the highest, and on earth peace and good will to men." Around the bottom was cast the inscription, "Proclaim Liberty throughout the land to all the inhabitants thereof."

A new clock was also presented by Seybert. This was made by the (Seth) Thomas Clock Company of Thomaston, Conn.

When the new clock and bell were installed in the State House the Lukens clock and Wilbank bell were stored.

In 1847 the citizens of the Borough of Germantown talked of building a town hall. In anticipation of consolidating the borough with the City of Philadelphia in 1854, a town hall was actually built. This building was used as a hospital during the Civil War.

In 1877 the old steeple of the Germantown town hall was torn down and replaced by a tower. The Lukens clock and Wilbank bell were placed in this tower as a gift to the citizens of Germantown.

At 9:00 o'clock on the morning of October 4, 1877, the hundredth anniversary of the Battle of Germantown was celebrated by one hundred strokes on the Wilbank bell, and at noon the Lukens clock was started.

With the passage of time, the old town hall fell into decay and a new building was built directly in front of the old one. This white marble building was completed in 1923 and dedicated in 1925. A prominent feature is a clock tower in which the Lukens clock and Wilbank bell were placed, having been removed from the old building. They are still doing service.

13

CHRISTIAAN HUYGENS

ACCURATE timekeeping, as it is known today, had its real beginning in December 1656, when Christiaan Huygens invented the pendulum-controlled clock. Huygens achieved a high standing in mathematics, astronomy, and other sciences, yet, throughout his busy life, he directed much of his time and effort to perfecting his clocks. He, probably more than any man before him, applied science to timekeeping.

No comprehensive history of science could be written without mention of Huygens, and no history of clocks should even be contemplated without an understanding of this man and his work.

Christiaan Huygens was born in The Hague in 1629, the second son of Constantijn Huygens, a well-known poet and statesman, as important in his field as his son proved himself in science. The son studied law and mathematics at Leiden University (1645–1647) and continued his studies at Breda (1647–1649).

He then settled in The Hague until 1666. There he devoted himself to mathematical, mechanical, physical, and astronomical studies. Besides inventing the pendulum clock, Huygens during these years developed the theory of probabilities, advanced theoretical and geo-metrical optics (lens grinding), and discovered the rings of Saturn and its satellite Titan.

According to his own statement, Huygens invented the pendu-lum-controlled clock "late in 1656" and made it available to the people of Holland "a few months later." He was granted a patent by the Sen-ates of the United Provinces in June 1657. Huygens published his now very rare pamphlet *Horologium* in 1658, in which he set forth his claim for the invention and explained it. This work is not to be con-fused with Huygens's much better known masterpiece, *Horologium Oscillatorium*, which did not appear until 1673. Of this, more will be said later.

Fewer than ten copies of the *Horologium* seem to have survived. At least two are in the United States. One is in the Yale University Library, and one in the private collection of Mr. Penrose R. Hoopes. Incidentally, the Yale copy once belonged to William Molyneux. A copy of the *Horologium* is in the possession of a private collector in England, and there are copies in Leiden and Paris.

This original treatise on the pendulum clock is here made available in English. (See page 97.) It is a milestone in horological literature, and reading it will give a better understanding of timekeeping.

By Huygens's day the problem of accurate timekeeping was rather fully realized. Others had given great thought to it: as early as 1530, Gemma Frisius of Louvain had pointed out that the way to deter-mine longitude on ship board was by means of an accurate chro-nometer.

The great Galileo's pioneer work with the pendulum is well known; he actually conceived the idea of regulating a clock by a pen-dulum. But he was old and blind when he conveyed the plan to his son, Vincenzio, who did not succeed in constructing an accurate pendulum-controlled clock, it seems.

The pre-Huygens clocks depended upon the foliot—a swinging bar—for control and regulation. The foliot never had a definite period of swing or vibration, and a clock so constructed could only approxi-mate accuracy and might vary as much as an hour or two in a day. For the three centuries before Huygens this sort of timekeeping was sufficiently accurate for the everyday life of the people but was of little or no value to the scientist.

The pendulum did have a fixed period of vibration and gave a scientific accuracy to timekeeping. The use of the pendulum in clocks was not confined to those used by astronomers but rapidly spread to all clocks. In this way a great scientific invention almost immediately found its way into practical use.

The reader will be astonished by some of Huygens's statements regarding the pendulum; they reflect the rather incomplete knowledge of the theory in 1656. In the following two decades, Huygens thoroughly mastered the theory and practice of the pendulum. But from the very beginning he realized the difficulties involved in reconciling the clock pendulum in practice to the laws of the simple theoretical pendulum of the mathematician.

In his first pendulum-controlled clock, that of 1656 shown in the *Horologium*, Huygens recognized the fact that a wide-swinging pendulum, necessary when the verge escapement was used, would introduce errors. He ingeniously cut down the arc of swing by introducing certain wheels.

But even between 1656, when this first pendulum clock was invented, and 1658, when the *Horologium* appeared, Huygens discovered that one way of overcoming the difficulty in having the clock pendulum follow the laws of the theoretical pendulum would be to make it travel in a path other than the arc of a circle.

A clock in the National Museum of the History of Science at Leiden bears the following inscription on a small brass plate under the dial: "Salomon Coster Haghe met privilege 1657." This is probably the oldest pendulum clock still in existence. The interesting feature of this clock is that it is provided with curved cheeks to give the pendulum a path other than that of the arc of a circle. But the cheeks are not yet of cycloidal form—the form needed to give the pendulum the path mathematically set down by the theory.

Although Huygens knew as early as 1657 that cheeks must be applied, it was not until the end of 1659 that he determined the mechanical properties of the cycloid and the correct form of the cheeks.

In 1666 Huygens accepted an invitation from the French states-man Colbert to settle in Paris as a member of the newly formed *Académie des Sciences*. He continued to live in Paris until 1681.

In Paris he published in 1673 one of his masterpieces, *Horologium Oscillatorium*, dedicated to Louis XIV. In this book he described his improved pendulum clock, among other things. By now, Huygens had thoroughly mastered the theory of the pendulum and had supplied his clock with cheeks of the proper cycloidal form.

In 1675 Huygens invented the balance wheel and spiral spring for watches, bringing to portable timepieces an accuracy comparable to that of pendulum-controlled clocks. This invention has been claimed also for Dr. Robert Hooke, of England. Actually, the invention was of sufficient importance to give honor to both men.

One of Huygens's greatest scientific achievements was his wave theory of light, which he communicated to the *Académie* in 1678. This was published in 1690 in a small book, *Traité de la Lumière*. Huygens returned to The Hague in 1681 and continued his interest in science and clocks until his death in 1695.

Opposite. Huygens's improved clock. When Huygens invented his first pendulum clock, he already realized errors that might be caused by the wide swing of the pendulum necessary with the arrangement he used. In his clock of 1656 (see page 101) he tried to overcome the errors by in-troducing certain wheels and was partly successful. Even before he pub-lished his pamphlet on this clock, he realized that to have absolute accu-racy with a wide-swinging pendulum, it would be necessary to make the bob travel a path that was not the arc of a circle. He worked toward this in a clock made in 1657 (and still extant; see page 133), in which he introduced cheeks; the suspension of the pendulum striking these cheeks caused the bob to travel in a path not an arc of a circle. Finally he com-pletely mastered the theory and practice of the curve known as the cycloid and in his final clock, here shown, gave the cheeks the proper mathematical form. The upper part of the pendulum suspension was of silk cords, and conformed to the shape of the cheeks. By this means he made a clock, the pendulum of which followed absolute mathematical laws; the bob of this pendulum traveled a path of a cycloidal curve. The width of the pendulum swing no longer mattered. Swings were made in equal intervals of time no matter how wide they might be.

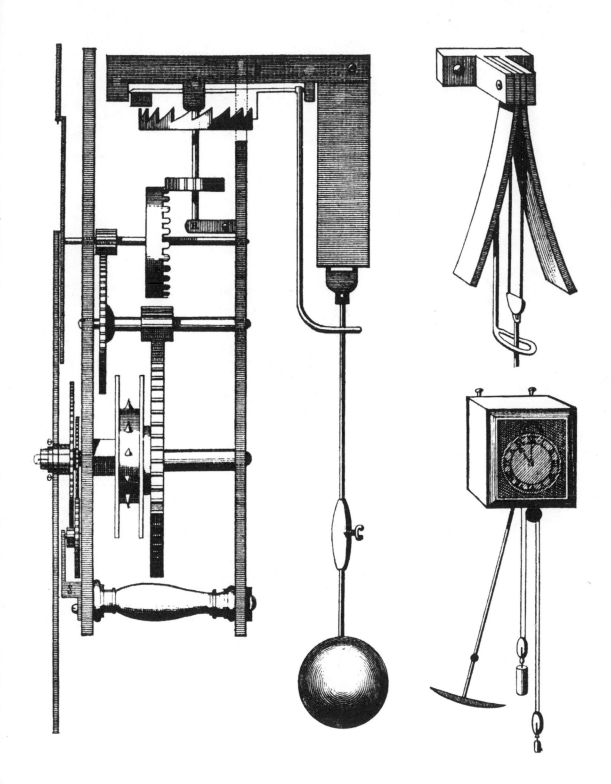

CHRISTIANI

HVGENII à ZVLICHEM,

CONST. F.

HOROLOGIVM.

HAGÆ COMITVM·

Ex officina Adriani Vlacq.

M. DC. LVIII.

CHRISTIAAN HUYGENS OF ZULICHEM
TO HIS LORDS
THE MOST POWERFUL AND ILLUSTRIOUS SENATORS
OF HOLLAND AND FRISIA
GREETINGS BESPEAKING
EVERY SUCCESS!

We are told that the first sun dial in Rome was one which, along with other booty, was brought from a certain captured town in Sicily and set up in a public place, 477 years after the founding of the city. When the people of Rome, out of necessity and for want of a better, had conducted their affairs according to this for 99 years, although it had manifestly not been designed for the region of Latium* and accordingly displayed markings out of harmony with the hours—the censor Quintus Marcius Philippus finally set up alongside it one that was more carefully adjusted, and this service was acknowledged most gratefully among his acts as censor.

As one doing a similar thing in the present day, and of no less advantage to the public insofar as I have rectified the instability of clocks not only in one city but of all everywhere, I should have thought, most noble sirs, that I might likewise have expected a gratitude similar to that which Quintus Marcius received from his fellow citizens. This might have been expected if only original nobility of nature and sincerity were in evidence again for a time on the earth, in the way that both things and events of the same kind are wont to recur after intervals. But since these virtues have long since become extinct among the majority of men and since imposture and misrepresentation in regards to others holds sway, I, on my part, readily saw what fate awaited my invention once it should have begun to be generally known, and my surmise did not mislead me.

Even in this, our own country, the audacity and shamelessness of certain persons asserted itself to the extent that, nowise deterred by your prohibition, they have dared to alter the invention as gotten from me and then to proclaim it as something entirely new and better than

---

* Latium: the region of north Italy around Rome.

mine. Those who have witnessed these injustices done me in my presence, and before my eyes, have admonished me that there is danger of results by no means better from foreign quarters.

They say that inordinately envious men will arise also in foreign lands and make prey of this fame-bringing achievement of mine, small as it is: men who would try to persuade, if not even themselves, at least the world at large, that these things are not due to the talent of the citizens of our country, but were the products, much earlier, of some one of their own countrymen.

Since the injustice of this matter seemed to have reference to our whole people, and therefore to you also, most illustrious lords, who have never borne it with tranquil spirit that credit for inventions (the most notable being the printing press and telescope) was diverted from your Holland by the deceit of plagiarists—I confess that I have been goaded by no small degree of zeal to assert for Holland the honor of this invention of mine.

Thus, pursuing the only course which seemed to lie open toward this goal, I, as the author himself of the new machine, have undertaken a description of the whole plan of it and a declaration to the world of its having been constructed. This has been done in a volume of small size, which might have been even shorter if I had not decided that answer should be given, as I went along, to objections which I foresaw would be leveled at me by some and which could challenge the very basis of my invention.

I come, with that respect which is fitting, to dedicate this modest work to your illustrious name and to entrust it to your care, since it could not see the light of day under better auspices. And I do not dedicate and consecrate these few pages and the invention itself as anything due to be even a little famous. Be indulgent, in accordance with your accustomed kindness, with one devoting his studies as best he knows how to the common good and who has no other thing more at heart than at a later date you may have occasion to approve his studies in a matter of great moment. May God keep safe the nation under your rule and prosper it!

**The Timepiece of Christiaan Huygens
of Zulichem, son of Constantijn**

Because of its extraordinary usefulness, there was no doubt that the way of computing time which I invented late in the year 1656, and began to make available to the people of our own country within a few months thereafter, would quickly spread far and wide. By now many replicas of the new device have been reproduced and sent in all directions.

However, I willingly comply with the suggestion of those who have proposed that I should present the idea embodied in written form. I do this to oblige those whom the idea might reach more slowly because of intervening distances; and to counteract the audacity of men of ill-spent idleness and keep them from preying upon the inventions of others and peddling them as their own—which is their custom.

The date of the bestowing of the grant from the exalted senators of the United Provinces, June 16, 1657, would refute these persons if there were need for it. Besides there are many whom I informed about the invention immediately it was brought forward. These might serve as witnesses.

The pendulum of the astronomers was the basis of my invention. This will be surmised by anyone familiar with the fact that the pendulum has been used by astronomers for some years. With water clocks, and whatever other self-operating means they had been accustomed to use in their observations, failing them, they at length began practicing a method of time measurement first taught by that ingenious man, Galileo Galilei.

This method was as follows: Impulse was given by hand to a weight suspended from a thin chain. The oscillations were counted and tallied with the same number of time intervals of equal duration. By this method they carried out observations of eclipses more painstakingly than before and measured the diameter of the sun with considerable success as well as the distances of the stars.

The motion of the pendulum, however, ceased unless repeatedly supplemented by the action of a person standing by. The task of counting the swings of the pendulum to and fro proved wearisome. Certain persons, with admirable patience, stayed on watch entire nights to keep pendulums in motion and count the swings while observations were being made.

Seeing this to be a most even kind of motion and practically the only kind given in nature which could be translated into construction of a mechanical sort, I pondered how one might arrive at the same result and also find a remedy for the twofold inconvenience mentioned above. Having weighed various kinds of construction in my mind I finally selected the one which I am about to present as being more intelligible and practicable than others.

Once this invention has been taken up and converted to public and private use, as already has been done, it will benefit all mankind because an agreement of clocks with one another will be possible, and of clocks with the sun itself, to a degree never witnessed before and indeed almost to as full an extent as could be hoped for.

Astronomers will be relieved of the burden of keeping the pendulums in motion and the task of counting the swings. Such matters as the unequal lengths of days from noontime to noontime may be studied more carefully. Persons presuming to deny that days were equal from noontime to noontime have hitherto been refuted by reasoning rather than by experiment productive of certainty.

There are those who agree with me that the practical application of the scientific knowledge of longitude to navigation can only be attained by clocks carried through the seas, clocks that are most skillfully devised and free from every aberration. But this matter will receive my attention, or that of others, at another time.

I shall now submit my self-operating machine to your scrutiny by means of a drawing and shall clearly explain the drawing in words as well as I am able.

Two oblong plates of equal size, AB and CD, comprise the foundation part of the construction. Into these, from both sides, are inserted the arbors of the wheels. These plates are discernible in the plan only by their edges. I have deliberately omitted the four posts by which they are joined at the corners lest these obstruct a view of the other parts.

Summary of working of Huygens's clock of 1656. Controlling Element: the pendulum SIT (approximately 9.78 inches long). The period of a pendulum of this length is ½ second per single swing from left to right; and ½ second for the swing back from right to left; or one second for a complete oscillation. Hence this pendulum makes 3600 (60 x 60) complete oscillations in an hour; or 7200 swings or half oscillations.

The Wheel E (72 teeth) in one turn gives Pinion G (6 leaves) 12 turns; it also gives the Wheel H (72 teeth) 12 turns; H gives the Pinion K (6 teeth) 144 turns (12 x 12) to one turn of E.

Therefore this also gives the Crown Wheel, L, 144 turns. L has 25 teeth so that it engages the upper pallet M and the lower pallet N 3600 (144 x 25) times each for every single revolution of E. Hence it will be seen that while the pendulum SIT makes 3600 complete oscillations in an hour, the wheel E will make one revolution in an hour.

The Minute Hand Ψ is attached to the axis of the Wheel E. Since E turns once in an hour, Ψ also turns once in an hour. The dial under Ψ is divided into 60 parts to mark minutes.

The Hour Hand: The Pinion V (6 teeth) is attached to the axis of the Wheel E and, like E, turns once in an hour. V drives the Wheel X (72 teeth) and X turns once in twelve hours. The Hour Hand Λ is connected with the axis of X and also turns once in twelve hours. The dial under Λ is marked into 12 parts for the hours.

The Second Hand Σ is attached to the axis of the Wheel H. Since H makes 12 turns in an hour—one turn every 5 minutes—Σ also makes 12 turns in an hour. The dial under Σ is marked first into 5 parts, and each of these 5 parts in turn is marked into 60 parts, indicating seconds. Thus the dial under Σ is divided into 300 parts, marking seconds (5 x 60).

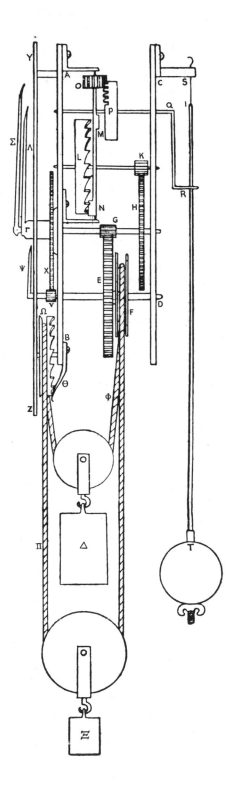

The first wheel is E, to the arbor of which is also affixed the small wheel F. Around F is wound a rope with the suspended weight Δ, in the manner which I shall later describe.

The wheel E is thus turned by the force of this weight. It [E] turns the next nearest wheel H; and this turns the wheel L, the teeth of which are shaped to the likeness of the teeth of a saw.

In proximity to the arbor of L stands, upright, the arbor MN,* having attached to it two small plates or "ears," with one of which the upper, and with the other of which the lower, teeth of the wheel L come in contact. This is with a constant variation so that as the wheel L turns in a circle, this upright arbor, MN, is not brought around to a full turn or revolution, but is worked back and forth with an alternating movement, now in this direction now in that.

I refrain from expounding this process in greater detail because it may be witnessed in clocks which are in common use, from which clocks this invention of mine does not thus far differ—though differ it does, and very much, in the details which follow.

On the arbor MN is imposed the pinion O, into the teeth of which are fitted the teeth of the wheel P. These latter are teeth of the kind which our craftsmen call "crown style." There is no need that the wheel P be tooth-edged on the whole of its circumference. It is only necessary that it be tooth-edged on its upper part.

The pinion O, like the arbor MN to which it is fastened, has a movement that alternates backward and forward and it activates the wheel P with a like kind of motion. Since the diameter of P is greater than that of the pinion O, it follows that the wheel rotates upon a lesser portion of its orbit than the pinion does. Toward what end this is directed I shall point out elsewhere.

The arbor of the wheel P extends somewhat beyond the plate CD and has attached to it the small crutch QR. This crutch QR is bent at its lower end and at the point R is bored out so that through this fairly ample opening the bronze rod IT may freely pass.

This rod IT, at its upper part, is held suspended at S by a wire, while from its lower end it supports the weight T, which weight is

* The upright "arbor MN" is the verge. (Author.)

forced upward or descends downward (as there is need of this) by the turning of a shell-shaped washer beneath it.

Now that these matters have been explained in order that the pattern of movement, and indeed the pattern of the invention as a whole, may be grasped, it is first of all to be noted that if the pendulum SIT had not been passed through the opening R, and were simply lacking, then the crutch QR would be driven to and fro in rapid agitation by the force of the weight Δ as it set all the wheels of the machine in motion.

The rod IT (with the weight T appended) having, however, been passed through the opening R, the said agitation of the crutch or lever is thus impeded and the whole clock remains at rest until the weight T, given a single impulse, brings about a beginning of motion.

Once this has happened the pendulum SIT is carried along parallel to the plate CD in a motion of an oscillating kind. The crutch QR, feeling as it does the propelling force of the weight Δ, goes along, on its own, with the movement of the pendulum in such a way as to aid the pendulum in its successive oscillations. And thus the movement of the pendulum is rendered lasting, for it would quickly lessen and tend to rest if the pendulum were not attached to the clock.

At each double swing, or complete oscillation, of the pendulum there will be noted an equivalent number of ticking sounds, two such sounds for each oscillation or one sound for each swing. These sounds, or ticks, are caused by the impact of the wheel L against the small plates on MN. Such are the aspects of my machine which particularly need explaining, for the sum of the whole invention centers on this action.

In the plan there is a third plate, YZ, parallel to those earlier mentioned and separated by an intervening space from the plate AB. In this space is seen the tooth-edged pinion V which has a common arbor with the wheel E.

Fitted into V are the teeth of the wheel X, which [X] has fixed to its center the hollow tube Γ, which, in turn, extends beyond the plate YZ and carries attached to it the main hand of the clock Λ.

Another hollow tube is located within the tube Γ, this being the arbor on which the wheel X turns,* and through it passes the arbor of the wheel H. This hollow tube is inserted in the plate AB and extends through the plate YZ.

To the end of the arbor of the wheel H, which passes through this second hollow tube, is attached another hand , longer than the hand Λ. This Σ indicates the secondary time elements or seconds.

An indicator of the primary time elements, or minutes, viz.: Ψ which is much shorter than either of the aforementioned hands, is attached to the end of the arbor DV, this having been brought forward beyond the plate YZ. And this small indicator travels close to the plate YZ, marking off each minute in a small circle. Above this the hour hand Λ turns, and above that finally the indicator Σ, which I shall call the second hand.

Though these details—and also the placement of the [wheels and] pinions and the number of teeth in them—can be varied in many ways, I deem it sufficient to propose as a model the following numbering, which is one tested by experience. Accordingly, I shall designate the total of teeth in each pinion, figures which seemed to suit this design best.

There are seventy-two (72) teeth on the circumference of each of the wheels E and H, and six (6) leaves each on the pinions G and K. The wheel L has twenty-five (25) teeth and the pinion O has ten (10). The wheel P has twenty (20) teeth or only part of that number because, as I said, there is no necessity that this entire wheel be incised in tooth fashion.

The length of the pendulum SIT is about five-sixths of a Rhineland foot (which closely approximates the old Roman). † Each successive single swing of this pendulum is marked by a period of one-half second. The pendulum may be adjusted either by comparison with the sun or with other clocks of the same sort. This length of pendulum is in accord with the wheels as arranged. It is capable of producing the

---

* The wheel X turns freely on the second hollow tube, which serves as an "axle" for it. (Author.)

† The Rhineland foot was equivalent to 31.39 cms. or 12.358 inches. "About" five-sixths of a Rhineland foot would be equivalent evidently to 9.78 inches, the length of the half-seconds pendulum. (Author.)

equality of movement desired and is sufficient even for astronomical uses.

If, nevertheless, a pendulum four times as long, or longer, should be used, with the introduction of larger wheels, greater delicacy of adjustment might be obtained and we could rely more safely on the slower oscillations of the pendulum for accuracy. I have already seen extra-long pendulums of this sort used with notable success in large public clocks; in one place one of twelve feet,* in another, one of twenty feet, with a disc of twenty-five or thirty pounds attached.

But returning to what was set forth in our plan, it is evident that when the wheel E is rotated once, the wheel H is rotated twelve times. L, which follows H (through K), is turned 144 times for each single revolution of E. Since L has twenty-five teeth it acts alternately upon the small plates M and N in 3600 instances and the pendulum SIT makes a corresponding number of double swings (or complete oscillations). †

Since there are 3600 seconds contained in an hour, the wheel E makes one rotation therefore in an hour's time. For this reason the circle underlying the indicator Ψ also is divided into 60 parts to signify minutes.

And because the wheel H—and the indicator Σ along with it—completes twelve turns within an hour (i.e., once every five minutes), I therefore divide the circle underlying Σ, first into 5 parts, and then these several parts into sixty smaller ones to denote seconds.

Finally, within its circle the indicator Λ ought to designate twelve hours, and hence in order that it may revolve once in twelve hours' time, to the pinion V are given six teeth and to the wheel X seventy-two.

I shall now explain the way in which the weights Δ and Ξ are ap-

---

* A two-seconds pendulum would be 156.56 inches (about 13 feet) long. Since Huygens was using the Rhineland foot, he was evidently speaking of such a pendulum. A pendulum twenty feet long would have a period of swing of almost two and one-half seconds. (Author.)

† In one hour (3600 seconds) a pendulum 9.78 inches long will make 3600 complete oscillations or 7200 half oscillations or swings. A clock fitted with such a pendulum will, therefore, have 7200 "ticking sounds" per hour. (Author.)

pended to the clock. For by a new device I have so arranged it that when the principal weight Δ is drawn upward, the movement of the clock neither ceases nor is in anywise impeded. This was particularly necessary in this invention in order that no moment of time be subtracted, or the movement of the pendulum be slowed up, while the weight was being raised.

There is provided a rope which is continuous and reverting upon itself with end attached suitably to end. This, after first having encircled the pulley F (which has been rendered rough with pointed tips of iron so that the rope will cling better), then encircles the under side of the block to which the principal weight Δ is attached.

Rising from here it passes over the pulley Ω and again descending supports a second block with the lesser weight Ξ appended. From here it returns once more to F.

The pulley Ω—which for purpose of illustration I here have suspended between the plates AB and YZ, whereas otherwise it is wont to be affixed more conveniently to the case which encloses the whole clock—has at one circling edge small teeth wrought in iron, as in the wheel L, and pressing against these from above it has the spring Θ, from which follows the fact that it can be turned only in the other direction, viz., when the rope Π has felt traction and the weight Δ on that account ascends.

The trough running around the circumference of this pulley ought to be so hollowed out as to somewhat confine the inserted rope and to restrain it from slipping when the pulley is not in motion. The weight Ξ is also employed for the same purpose.

With these elements so arranged, Δ will always weigh upon the rope with half its weight and will maintain motion for the clock even when the rope is feeling traction and the weight is being raised.

Up to this point I have been explaining details which pertain to the structure of the machine. It remains for me to make clear to what extent it excels all those that have been in use to the present day.

It is quite well known that there are causes of error and unbalance in the other clocks. For notable irregularity of movement follows immediately upon even the slightest mistake in regard to the proper placement and filing of the wheels. Then too the hours run more slowly when the oil which is wont to be put on the arbors has dried out and is decreasing. Though these defects be lacking, clocks still experience (nay! sometimes anticipate) the various changes of the atmosphere and of the seasons of the year: they are generally found to be slower because of cold and run faster than normal by reason of heat.

Since it is indeed the distinction and advantage of the pendulum that it always necessarily moves with the same even tenor except upon a change of length, it is surely apparent that by my invention I have completely done away with all these disadvantages which I have mentioned, so much so that unless there should intervene an impeding force of such a kind that the whole action of the clock would be stopped by it, no slowing down or irregularity of the clock's movement is to be feared.

Some may doubt this for two reasons; first: because this pendulum of mine—experiencing as it does a certain force and pressure of the crutch QR upon each of its movements to and fro—would seem to be different from a free pendulum; and second, because—even though it should retain the properties of, and be in every respect on a par with, the simple pendulum—two shortcomings of the free pendulum itself have been noted by some few persons who have investigated such matters with thoroughgoing accuracy of detail.

I do not deny that what is said about pressure from the crutch is true. But I know this to be pressure of the very slightest kind by reason of the gravitational weight of T, which is so well balanced that the swinging of the pendulum all but stops, yet keeps on going by as small a margin as possible—still, a margin ever the same. Hence its swinging motion goes on no faster nor any the less evenly than if the lever were no obstacle whatever, or than if SIT, as a simple pendulum, were being given impulse by hand, as has been accustomed to be done up until now. And experience confirms this very well.

As for the two shortcomings of the pendulum itself which they call attention to, some people deny them outright. One of them I admit, but as one posing scarcely any opposition to my clock; the other I declare completely void of substance.

Thus they truly assert the following; that broader and shorter swings of the same pendulum do not take place within a perfectly equal amount of time, but the former take a little longer than the latter. This can be demonstrated by an easy experiment. For if two pendulums, equal in weight and length, should be moved away from the perpendicular, one much and the other little, on having been released simultaneously they will not be seen traveling in the same direction together for long, but the one whose swings are smaller will vary sooner. But my clock, as I have said, is less liable to this shortcoming from the fact that all its oscillations travel an equal distance outward from the perpendicular.

In the discussion of my clock it is necessary that we pursue the minutest particulars. Sometimes it happens, either from a change in weather or through some defect in the machine, that the crutch QR is not always moved back and forth with the same force. As a result the oscillations of the pendulum increase or decrease though by only a small difference. Since longer swings of the pendulum take more time than shorter ones, a certain degree of irregularity would follow in the action of the clock.

No matter how negligible all this may seem, we had difficulty in finding a remedy for it as long as clocks were so constructed that the swinging of the pendulum was rather wide. I obviated the need for a remedy by introducing the pinion O and the wheel P. By means of these I brought it about that though the swings of the pendulum were shorter, the axle MN would not be affected thereby in its reciprocal motion.

For instance, the diameter of the wheel P is made two or three times greater than the diameter of the pinion O. It follows, therefore, that upon an oscillation of P, though small, O still completes a sufficiently great portion of its circuit. With shorter oscillations performed in this way, even though some of them, at times, may exceed others in breadth, experience has shown that the time of successive oscillations differs by no notable margin.

Because of this fact, even with the weight of Δ increased to double, the motion of the pendulum is not thereby accelerated nor the running of the clock altered. The result was otherwise in all other clocks in frequent use up until now.

Gottfried Wendelin, a man famous for his astronomical studies, is, I believe, the first and only one who has publicly declared the second shortcoming of the pendulum, saying in writing that he himself had found from experiment that the oscillations of this sort of pendulum were greater in winter than in summer and this by a notable difference.*

But since he acknowledges that in his investigation he used only sand clocks and unscientific devices, which were perhaps designed with not too much care, many have doubted how accurate his findings might be. I have not observed any such thing myself. To the contrary, both in smaller clocks in which the pendulum is half a foot long and in larger ones where it equals almost 24 feet, I have found the same length to be present at the time of winter solstice and in midsummer. But this length ought to be longer in winter by at least one-seventh part of itself if the opinion of Wendelin were true.

With the balance and constancy of my invention having been declared I shall now put an end to the description, leaving to the industry of the craftsmen the many things which could be added. For the craftsmen, having been instructed regarding the nature of the invention, will discover without difficulty how it can be applied to clocks of various kinds and even to those clocks long since fashioned after an ancient form.

In the shop of the man whose efforts I first employed in making these clocks I saw such clocks as were moved not by a weight but by the force of a spring. Though formerly in these there was need of the well-known fusee and the cord wrapped around it, with the help of which the first and last impulses of the spring were made equal; with these aids omitted teeth are now added to the drum itself in which the spring is enclosed. Although the movement of the pendulum is not in this way equally strong at the end as at the beginning, the oscillations do not become slower at the end as has been previously demon-

---

* At first glance it would seem that Wendelin was referring to the change in length of the pendulum due to temperature: but he had something far different in mind. (Author.)

strated. The spring, in the part where it is wound at the center, is tensed and care is thus taken lest at any moment of time the action of the clock should be clogged.

I pass over the fact that he has devised machines of this kind which make the hours known by sound: in such wise that both parts, the one prepared for this and the one which turns the hands of the clock, were moved by one and the same weight or spring. All these things pertain to my invention in no other way than that it provided them with occasion and opportunity.*

Finis

* While this translation was in progress, a translation by Ernest L. Edwardes appeared independently in the *Horological Journal,* official organ of The British Horological Institute, Vol. 96, Numbers 1150 and 1151, July and August 1954. A comparison of these translations is interesting. These are the only English versions of the *Horologium* known to the author.

14

ASPECTS OF TIME

No matter how well and accurately a clock was made, it was necessary to regulate and set it. This could only be done by comparison with an accepted time standard. If this standard was another clock, then that clock in turn, either directly or indirectly, had to be set and regulated by comparison with the basic time standard—the duration of the earth's rotation on its axis, which marked the day. This could only be accomplished by reference to some celestial body—the sun or a star. And this involved the science of astronomy.

Today, time is accurately measured in great astronomical observatories, and signals are sent out through the medium of radio. Before this the telegraph was used. Before the telegraph a woman in London who owned a very accurate watch which was the source of her livelihood, each day went to the Greenwich Observatory, set the watch, and carried this "time" to various clockmakers.

But the clockmakers of Colonial Pennsylvania had none of these conveniences. Some few, like David Rittenhouse, had the knowledge and instruments for making astronomical observations and calculating time from them. But the average clockmaker, no matter how skilled he might be as a craftsman, was forced to rely on other means.

Time, as it is understood today, was not too important in Colonial days. There were no trains and airplanes to catch, there were no schedules to keep. Cities and communities were more or less isolated from one another. There was no great necessity for communities as little as twenty miles apart to be accurately in step as far as time was concerned. It was sufficient that each place have the accurate time for that location.

How then did the average clockmaker finally set and regulate the clock he had finished? The sun dial, through the ages, had reached a high degree of development. If properly designed and built for a certain specific location, it was accurate in indicating a certain kind of time —solar or sun time. "Dialing"—the art and science of sun dials—was once a popular subject. Every community had a sun dial of some sort.

But certain corrections were necessary to translate solar time, as indicated by the sun dial, into mean time, necessary for regulating clocks. This will be covered fully, later in this chapter. But it is sufficient to say here that these corrections were arranged in tables, known as Equation of Time Tables, and that the old clockmakers were familiar with these and their use.

Very few sun dials have been found in the inventories of old clockmakers. This is quite understandable, because sun dials were quite common and the clockmaker found little need to own one of his own.

And there was still another convenient and quite accurate method whereby a clockmaker might set and regulate his clock from the sun by the observation of its rising. All that was needed was an almanac, a common book in Colonial times containing data calculated for various specific places and their environs. There were almanacs for Philadelphia, Baltimore, Boston, and other places. These almanacs gave the exact local time of sunrise for each day in the year.

The clockmaker, if he had a clear horizon, looked up the time of sunrise for a certain day. Then he observed the horizon, and when the sun actually rose he knew exactly what time it was and set his clock accordingly.

Astronomers in all ages realized that there was an inequality in the lengths of days as measured by the sun dial. But they disagreed on the reasons for this and on the calculations of the discrepancies. The invention of the pendulum clock in 1656 renewed interest in this subject, and Huygens suggested that his clock, with its accuracy, might help solve the problem.

John Flamsteed, the first Astronomer Royal, "put an end to the controversy" in a dissertation which finally appeared annexed to the posthumous works of Jeremiah Horrocks, published in 1673.

This, of course, was in Latin. The first English translation of Flamsteed's explanation of the Equation of Time seems to have appeared in William Molyneux's *Sciothericum Telescopium*, which was published in Dublin in 1686. This may well be the first complete explanation in English.

It would be difficult to overestimate the importance of the Equation of Time in the study and appreciation of horology. Through the courtesy of Humphry M. Smith, of the Royal Greenwich Observatory, it is possible to give the following simple explanation of the Equation of Time, solar time, sidereal or star time, and mean solar time, the "time" by which men live.

THE EQUATION OF TIME

The accepted basis of time measurement from the earliest days has been the duration of the earth's daily rotation on its axis. One complete revolution of the earth marks the day. The time required for the earth to make one complete revolution is, for all practical purposes, constant.

The earth itself may, therefore, be looked upon as the "wheel work" of the world's standard clock. The "dial" of this great clock is the vast bowl of the heavens, with the sun and stars the "numerals." The "hands" of this clock are the transit instruments of the astronomers.

A transit is a telescope so fixed in its bearings that it can only move up and down, from north to south, but cannot move from east to west. Stated in another way, this means that the transit can only move in the plane of the meridian. The meridian is a great circle in the skies passing through the north point of the horizon, the zenith, or point directly overhead, and the south point.

Ideally, to measure the duration of one complete rotation of the earth on its axis, the motion should be referred to a fixed point in space, as one refers the motion of a clock's hands to the fixed numerals on the dial.

Unfortunately there is no way of meeting this requirement, since there is no truly stationary point of reference in the heavens. Hence certain adjustments must be made. Man has been forced to accept the "dial" offered by nature and make his adjustments accordingly.

Solar time is measured by the apparent duration of the daily revolution of the earth upon its own axis in reference to the sun. This is the time indicated on sun dials. The rotation of the earth causes the sun and stars to appear to cross the heavens from east to west. The sun is said to rise each day in the east and set in the west. At the instant the sun is at its greatest height above the horizon, that is, when it crosses the meridian, it is solar noon.

For many centuries the sun dial had no rival as an accurate indicator of time, but with the improvement of the mechanical clock, largely through the introduction of the pendulum as the regulating device, it became more and more evident that the time—in hours, minutes, and seconds—between one solar noon and the next was not constant throughout the year, but varied.

Also it was necessary that each day, as measured by an accurate clock, should have just as many seconds as every other day, and that each second should be the same length as every other second. Hence a mean solar day was created, one that would be constant in length throughout the year and seasons. The length of this "artificial" mean solar day was the average of the lengths of all solar days in a year.

Solar noon is sometimes as much as 16 minutes, 18 seconds sooner than, and sometimes as much as 14 minutes, 26 seconds later than, mean noon. Only four times a year are solar and mean noon the same, and only four times a year do the sun dial and clock agree.

The difference between mean time and solar time is known as the Equation of Time. "Equation" is here used in its archaic sense of "correction" or "adjustment." These corrections are substantially constant from year to year, and tables have been prepared showing the correction for each day in a specific year. The tables served all practical purposes for clockmakers who were forced to regulate and set their clocks from sun dials.

The difference between mean noon, as shown on clocks, and apparent solar noon, as shown on the sun dial, is not due to any discrepancy from day to day in the time required for the earth to make one complete revolution on its axis. This time, as has been stated, is practically constant.

Why then is there a difference between mean time and solar time? This question can best be answered by explaining the two components that make up the Equation of Time. These components are known as the "component due to eccentricity" and the "component due to obliquity."

The component due to eccentricity:

The earth, in addition to turning on its own axis each day, travels around the sun in an elliptical path once each year. Since this path is elliptical, the earth is sometimes nearer and sometimes farther from the sun. Therefore the earth travels this path at varying speeds, because when it is nearer the sun it travels faster, due to the forces of gravity, and more slowly when farther from the sun. The motion of the earth is such that an imaginary line joining the earth and sun would sweep over equal areas in equal times.

If the distance between the earth and sun were constant, that is, if the path of the earth were a circle with the sun at its center, then this imaginary line would move at a constant speed.

But since the path is an ellipse, the length of the line is not constant, and the angular speed is greatest when the earth is nearest the sun (at the beginning of January); at this time the solar day undergoes its greatest lengthening over the mean day. The correction, or adjustment, necessary to reconcile solar time to mean time from this cause is known as the "component due to eccentricity."

The component due to obliquity

Although the earth really travels in a path around the sun, to an observer on the earth the sun appears to travel through the heavens. The imaginary line along which the sun appears to move each year is known to astronomers as the ecliptic. Now the earth's axis is not per- pendicular, nor at right angles, to the plane of the ecliptic, but is "tilted." In short, the sun appears to travel through the heavens around the earth on a path, the plane of which intersects the plane of the earth's equator at an angle of $23° 27'$.

Therefore the sun is in the plane of the earth's equator only two times a year, at the vernal and autumnal equinoxes. Midway between these points the sun is at its greatest distance from the plane of the earth's equator, the summer and winter solstices. This is all due to the fact that the plane of the ecliptic—the imaginary line marking the sun's apparent path around the earth—intersects the plane of the earth's equator at an angle. The adjustment necessary to reconcile solar time to mean time due to this cause is known as the "component due to obliquity." The two components combined make up the Equation of Time.

SIDEREAL TIME

Sidereal time, star time, is based upon the duration of the earth's daily rotation on its axis as referred to a fixed star; or, to put it another way, upon the interval between two successive passages over- head of a fixed star. This is the time used by astronomers.

Although the stars themselves are moving through space at con- siderable speed and the whole solar system (including the earth) is moving, the stars are so far away that changes in their angular posi- tion are negligible.

In theory, any star might be used, but in practice it would be necessary to make observations of many stars and link these observa- tions together. The astronomers therefore use a hypothetical fixed point in space, the first point of Aries. Complications arise because the first point of Aries itself is not fixed but moving slowly westward among the stars. Calculations are therefore made to obtain a "fixed" first point of Aries.

The mean sidereal day is 3 minutes, 56 seconds *shorter* than the mean solar day, and in a year this amounts to one day. There is also the difficulty that sidereal time does not keep in step with periods of light and darkness.

The mean sidereal day is in itself divided into hours, minutes, and seconds. Because it is shorter than the mean solar day, the sidereal second is shorter than the mean solar second which is measured by the standard clock. Any clock can be adjusted to keep sidereal time by an adjustment of the pendulum. For instance, at London, a clock to keep accurate mean solar time should have a pendulum 39.14 inches long. To keep sidereal time this pendulum should be 38.93 inches long.

Mean time clocks can be best regulated by using the stars as reference points. The sidereal time of the astronomer is converted into mean solar time for general use.

STANDARD TIME

The creation of an "artificial" or imaginary sun solved the problem of mean time, but progress in rapid travel brought about by the railroad, and almost instantaneous communication by telegraph presented a new problem in timekeeping.

Mean noon occurs when the imaginary sun crosses the meridian. But as we travel eastward or westward on the earth's surface there is a different meridian for each place. So noon at Philadelphia is 4 minutes and 35 seconds later than in New York.

This meant very little when it took two days to travel between the two cities by stage coach. Each city and town could be content with the local time at that place. But when railroad travel became common it meant that a passenger traveling eastward or westward would have to change his watch every few minutes if he wished to be accurate. The old clockmakers working in Colonial times probably never thought of this problem; if they did, it meant little to them.

However, it was solved by dividing the nation into four time belts centered approximately at the meridians for 75°, 90°, 105° and 120° longitude west of Greenwich. The local times from belt to belt differ exactly one hour. So only four kinds of standard time are used in the United States: Eastern, Central, Mountain, and Pacific. This scheme was worked out first by the railroads and was universally adopted in the United States in 1870. In crossing westward from one time belt to the next, one's watch must be set back an hour, and it must be set forward the same amount when traveling eastward.

The next chapter will give a brief account of the life of William Molyneux, together with the text of his article "Concerning the Astronomical Equation of Time." More should be known about this great Irish scholar and patriot. He is mentioned in this book on Pennsylvania clocks because he stands as a symbol of the forces of liberty in thought and government which came to life in the latter part of the seventeenth century and resulted in the founding of Pennsylvania as well as in the progress of science. William Penn first came in contact with Quakerism in Ireland and it may be said that it was there that Pennsylvania was conceived.

The original text of Molyneux's article has been adhered to, but in order to facilitate reading, it has been broken up into short paragraphs, and in places archaic spelling has been supplanted by modern. Gratitude is hereby expressed to Dr. James Stokley for having carefully read over the revised manuscript and for his kind help and suggestions.

The biographical sketch is based on material supplied through the courtesy of Dr. David S. Torrens of Trinity College, Dublin.

15

WILLIAM MOLYNEUX

WILLIAM MOLYNEUX was a true patriot and industrious toiler, devoted to the best interests of those who lived in his country and age. He was born in Dublin, April 17, 1656. His father, Samuel Molyneux, was an expert in gunnery and wrote a treatise on the subject. The son was of delicate constitution from infancy and was educated at home.

He entered Trinity College, Dublin, in April 1671, at the age of fifteen, as a Fellow Commoner and graduated B.A., in the Hilary (January–March) term of 1674. His leanings were toward mathematics and the natural sciences, but he decided to study law. In 1675 he went to London, where he became a member of the Middle Temple.

In London he became greatly interested in the Royal Society and was elected a member. He returned to Dublin in 1678 and married. In 1680 he published a translation into English of a celebrated tract by the renowned philosopher René Descartes.

Molyneux began a correspondence with the Astronomer Royal, John Flamsteed, in 1681. Having an easy fortune, he was able to pursue his scientific researches, especially in the field of astronomy. During 1683 he became interested in forming a society in Dublin modeled after the Royal Society. This was the forerunner of the Royal Irish Academy.

He continued his interest in astronomy and in 1686 published his *Sciothericum Telescopium, or a New Contrivance for adapting a Telescope to an Horizontal Dial, for Observing the Movements of Time by Day or Night: useful in all Astronomical Observatories, and for regulating and adjusting curious Pendulum Watches and other Timekeepers, with proper Tables requisite thereto.*

From this work is taken the discussion of the equation of time on page 121.

In 1692 he became a Master of Arts at Trinity College and was chosen to represent the University of Dublin in the Irish Parliament. These were troublesome days in Ireland and he arose as champion of the constitutional rights of the Irish. Molyneux received the degrees of LL.B. and LL.D. from his alma mater at the Trinity (April–June) term in 1693.

Finally, in the spring of 1698, appeared his great work, *The Case of Ireland's Being Bound by the Acts of Parliament in England Stated.* In this he put forth the rights of Ireland from the standpoints of history, law, policy, and nature.

There was much in common between Molyneux and Thomas Jefferson, who came after him. Both were scientists, yet, above all else, they were men ready to fight for liberty and risk their all in the struggle. Molyneux fought for liberty as a principle. In his *Case of Ireland Stated* he wrote:

I might say, indeed, to mankind: for 'tis the cause of the whole race of Adam that I argue: liberty seems to be the inherent right of all mankind: and on whatsoever ground one nation can challenge it to themselves, on the same reason may the rest of Adam's children expect it.

In this same work appeared words and thoughts prophetic of the American Declaration of Independence:

All men are by nature in a state of equality, in respect of jurisdiction and dominion, this I take to be a principle in itself so evident, that it stands in need of little proof.

William Molyneux died October 11, 1698, in his forty-third year.

CONCERNING THE ASTRONOMICAL EQUATION OF TIME

by William Molyneux

Being now upon the business of time, and the accurate observation thereof, so as therefore to regulate curious timekeepers, it will not be improper to our subject to say something of the inequality of natural days. This matter has exercised the thoughts of astronomers in all ages. Though all have allowed that there really is such an inequality, yet they have much disagreed in assigning its quantity, or demonstrating the reason and affection thereof; till at last our most learned and ingenious English astronomer, and my honored friend, Mr. John Flamsteed,* Math. Regius, has determined the controversy and by most evident demonstrations has put the matter beyond further dispute, clearly evincing both the reasons, affections and quantity of this inequality.

His dissertation concerning this is annexed and published at the end of Opera Posthuma Jeremiae Horoxcii,† London, 1673, from which, with my esteemed friend's leave, I shall present the reader with the following schemes and demonstrations.

On account of the sun's eccentricity from the center of the earth's annual orbit, the daily motion of the earth is sometimes faster and sometimes slower than the mean motion, and consequently the apparent day is sometimes longer, and sometimes shorter, than the mean day.

This inequality and the quantity of the difference of the equal, or

* John Flamsteed (1646–1719): Astronomer Royal and first director of Greenwich Observatory. (Author.)

† Jeremiah Horrocks (1614–1641): brilliant English astronomer, first to observe a transit of Venus across the sun in 1639. (Author.)

mean, day from the apparent is demonstrated in [Molyneux's] Fig. 13, according to the Copernican System.*

Let $A B P N$ be the great orbit in which the earth is yearly carried around the sun. The center of this orbit is at C. A is the aphelion, † or the earth's place at noon on that day it is in its aphelion, suppose the 18th of June. B is the earth's place at noon the following day. $A L$ is an assigned meridian of the earth.

The arc $A B$, or the angle $A C B$, is the mean motion of the earth from noon of a given day to noon of the day following. L is a point in the given meridian turned toward the sun. While the earth, in its orbit, is carried from A to B, this point is rolled by the daily rotation of the earth from L through O, in its first place A; to d in the second place B, and when the said point arrives at d it is manifest that the earth has performed a complete revolution about its axis. This is because the meridian $B d$, in its second position at B, is made parallel to $A L$, its yesterday's position at A.

But it is not apparent noon until the same point, by the earth's revolution, is brought to e, where it is turned directly opposite the sun.

That this time is not the same with the mean noon, will be proved because the earth has not yet performed its mean motion above its revolution. This would be a sufficient argument, but also the daily motions of the earth about the sun, and consequently the return of any meridian to the sun, are very unequal. Neither can they possibly be equal in respect to any point about which the earth is not carried equally, as is sufficiently manifest from the inspection of the scheme.

Wherefore the mean noon and equal time respects the point of mean motion, that is the center of the orbit C. And in our present instance is when the meridian, carried from e, arrives at f, where it is directly opposite the center of the orbit C. And when it has gained this position, the earth has performed its mean motion above a revolution requisite to complete a mean day.

For the arc df, or the angle dBf, is equal to the angle ACB, the

---

* Copernican System: named for Copernicus (1473–1545), who put forth the theory that the planets, including the earth, move in orbits around the sun as the center. (Author.)

† Aphelion: the point in the orbit or path of a planet farthest from the sun. (Author.)

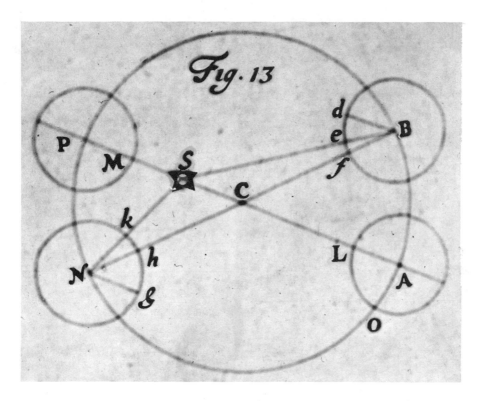

Fig. 13

mean daily motion of the earth. Also the arc *de*, which the earth, or any meridian therein, must pass more than a revolution before it is apparent noon, is equal to the angle *ASB*, the apparent meridian of the earth at the sun.

From whence it is evident that the arc *ef*, which the circumference of the rolling earth performs between the apparent and mean day, is equal to the angle *SBC*, which is the equation of the orbit.

Wherefore the prosthapaereses* of the orbit, resolved into portions of time, through this semicircle of anomaly † are negative, or to be subtracted from the apparent time, for herein the mean noon succeeds the apparent.

In like manner, if we take the opposite parts of the scheme, and consider the earth in its perihelion: ‡ the point *g*, or the meridian *Ng*,

* Prosthapaereses: the corrections necessary to find the "true."
† Anomaly: unevenness or inequality of motion. Present meaning in astronomy: the angular distance of a planet from its perihelion point as seen from the sun.
‡ Perihelion. That point in a planet's orbit nearest the sun. (Author.)

being parallel to its yesterday's position, the earth has performed one complete revolution.

This point being carried to *h*, where it is opposite the center of the orbit, it is now mean noon, for the arc *gh*, or the angle *gNh*, equals the mean daily motion of the earth passed over.

But it is not yet apparent noon until the earth, by its rotation, brings the same meridian to *k*, where it is directly opposite the sun. From whence it is manifest that the apparent day exceeds the mean day by so much time as it is requisite for the earth to pass through the arc *hk*, which arc is equal to the angle *CNS*.

The prosthapaeresis of the orbit being resolved into time, we have the equation of time, which throughout this semicircle of anomaly is affirmative, or to be added to the apparent time, because herein the mean noon precedes the apparent noon.

It is manifest from what has been said, that if the sun were in the center of the great orbit, and the earth's axis were not inclined to its path, or way, there would be no inequality of time, but the mean day and the apparent day would be equal.

Moreover, if there were no eccentricity of the sun from the center of the orbit, but there were the usual inclination of the earth's axis to the orbit, there would be no inequality of time such as is shown in the foregoing demonstration, yet there would arise another inequality from the said inclination of the earth's axis.

Or as the Ptolomaick * would express it, from the inclination of the ecliptic to the equator, the quantity and affections of which inequality is shown by the analemma.†

In [Molyneux's] Fig. 14, *PCF* is a quadrant of the solstitial colure.‡

* Ptolemy. Astronomer of Alexandria in the 2nd century A.D., who gave his name to the theory that the relative motion of the sun, moon and planets took place around the earth which was supposed to be stationary. Ptolemy did not originate this theory but published it in his book *The Almagest*. (Author.)

† Analemma. A sort of sun dial used in solving certain problems. The analemma has a figure-8-shaped graph showing the equation of time. (Author.)

‡ Solstitial colure. The great circle passing through the sky from the north pole to the south pole and through the solstices, the position occupied by the sun at the beginning of winter and of summer.

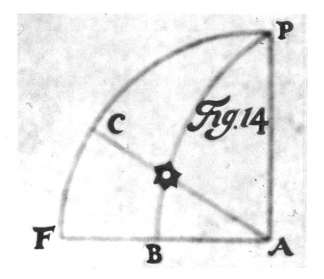

P is the pole. *AF* is a radius of the equator. *CA* is a radius of the ecliptic. *A* is the equinoctial point, or the place of the sun in the beginning of Aries ♈, at noon on some certain day.

⊙ is the sun's place at noon the following day, through which place, striking the arc *P* ⊙ *B*, perpendicular to the equator, *A* ⊙ will express the daily motion of the sun, and *AB* its right ascension, or the arc of the equator that culminates with the sun. Which arc, seeing it is one of the sides of a right triangle *A* ⊙ *B*, cannot be equal to the hypotenuse, that is the sun's motion *A* ⊙.

It is seen that the revolutions of the equator, and of its equal or like parts, are equable and performed in equal times. But the sun in passing equal parts of the ecliptic applies to the meridian with unequal parts of the equator. It therefore follows that solar days are unequal and that the difference between the sun's true place and its right ascension, being converted into time, is the true equation of time arising from this cause.

In the 1st and 3rd quadrants of the zodiac this equation is to be subtracted from the apparent time, for in them the longitude of the sun from the next equinoctial point passes the meridian sooner than a like arc projected in the equator.

But in the 2nd and 4th quadrants of the zodiac, this equation is to be added to the apparent time to get the mean: for in these the longitude of the sun from the equinox passes the meridian later than a like arc projected in the equator.

For example, let the longitude of the sun from the first point of Υ * be $\odot A$, 0°, 59′, 08″; its right ascension, or the arc of the equator culminating therewith, AB, 0°, 54′ 13″. Their difference, 4′ 55″, being converted into time is 00^h, 00^m, 19^{sec}, and by so much is the apparent day shorter than the mean.

This therefore is the equation of time arising from this cause, and is negative, or to be subtracted from the apparent time, to obtain the mean time. For the longitude of the sun arrives at the meridian sooner than a like arc projected in the equator.

Here are therefore demonstrated two sorts of equations of time arising from two different causes. If they are both to be added, or both to be subtracted, then their differences according to the nature of the greatest is to be added to or subtracted from the apparent time to get the mean.

Thus far I have presumed to borrow from my learned and ingenious friend's discourses, which is sufficient, I think, to put the matter out of dispute. After clearing the theory of this doctrine I next come to apply it to regulating curious timekeepers which are indeed very often abused for want of due consideration and right application of the equation of time.

For at some time of the year it happens that if our watches or oscillating pendulums do not differ above a quarter of an hour from the true showed by the sun or stars, they are false and need a correction.

And the reason for this is plain, for if our pendulum watch † goes true, it goes equal, that is, one 24 hours of any time of the year is as long as 24 hours at any other time of the year, and this perpetually and constantly.

That is, all watches that go true, measure equal or mean time, and

---

* The point where the sun in its apparent annual motion along the ecliptic crosses the equator from south to north is known as the vernal equinox or first point of Aries (Υ). (Author.)

† Pendulum watch. A watch with balance wheel provided with a spring and oscillating regularly, thus having the function of the pendulum of a clock. (Author.)

consequently ought to differ from the apparent time shown by a sun dial or other instrument, as much as the equation of time is in excess or defect. But the equation of time is sometimes above a quarter of an hour, therefore so much ought a good-going pendulum watch differ from the sun, if it be rightly adjusted.

But this will be more evident by explaining the tables.* These are calculated by the foregoing theory and will serve very well for these 20 years to come, though it must be confessed that, to have them most accurate, these tables ought to be calculated for every year, as is manifest to those who consider the foregoing theory.

Some few seconds of error there may be at the pains of calculating them himself, the method whereof he may find laid down in the forementioned treatise at the end of Horrocks's works, or in Mr. Flamsteed's "Doctrine of the Sphere" published in Sir J. Moore's *System of Mathematicks*.

We see that there are only four days in the year on which the equation of time ceases, that is, the apparent and mean day are the same, viz., on the 4th of April, the 6th of June, the 21st of August and the 13th of December.† If on any of these days we set a well-regulated pendulum watch to the apparent time shown by the sun or stars: on any day afterward it ought to differ from the apparent time shown by the sun by so much as the equation of time in the table indicates.

If the equation is to be subtracted, the pendulum ought to be so much slower (or behind) the sun: if the equation is to be added, the pendulum ought to be so much faster (or before) the sun. For on any day of the year observing the time exactly by the sun or stars, that time is the apparent time, and to gain the mean time which ought to be shown by the clock, we are to add to or subtract from the said apparent time, the equation answering the day of our observation.

Suppose, for instance, that on the 4th of April I observe the time by the sun, because the equation ceases when the apparent time and

* Molyneux here refers to the Equation of Time table. (Author.)

† The days in 1955 when the Equation of Time will be zero—when sun-dial noon and clock-time noon will be the same—are April 16, June 15, September 2, and December 26: according to *The American Ephemeris and Nautical Almanac*. (Author.)

mean time are the same; and therefore I set my clock to the exact and full time as the sun or stars show it. But if the pendulum go exactly true, and we move to the 4th of May, I shall find it 4′ 17″ behind the sun, for so much is the equation on the 4th of May to be subtracted from the apparent time of the sun, to give the mean time of the clock. That is, when the sun shows it to be 9 o'clock in the morning, the clock ought to be 8 hours, 55 minutes, 43 seconds.

And if I find the pendulum more or less behind the sun, it has not gone truly as it ought, but the pendulum, or swagg, is to be lengthened or shortened as is requisite to make it gain or lose the difference between the time shown by the clock and 8 hours 55′ 43″ in 30 days elapsed between the 4th of April and the 4th of May, according to the table whose use I shall declare presently.

But if the movement be exquisitely true, if it go to the 6th of June, it will again show the same time with the sun and stars, for then again the equation is nothing. And if it go onwards exactly to the 3rd of August, it will be 4′ 18″ before the sun, for at that time so much is the equation to be added to the apparent time to make it mean. Until again on the 24th of October the watch ought to be 16′ 4″ behind the sun, for so much is the equation that day subtracted.

Wherefore, if at any time we set our pendulum watch in order to rectify it, and bring it exactly to measure the mean day, we are to add to, or subtract from, the apparent time shown by the sun so much as the equation of days at the time we set it. For example, at noon, or just when the sun is on the meridian on the 9th of September, that is, when the apparent time is exactly at twelve o'clock, the equation is then 6′ 26″ subt. Wherefore I set my watch to 11 hours 53′ 34″.

Which, if it go right, that is, equally as it ought, on the 9th of October will be 14′ 52″ behind the sun. If it be either more or less behind or before the sun, it has gone false, and is to be rectified by either lengthening or shortening the pendulum as much as is required to make it gain or lose the difference between 14′ 52″ behind the sun, and its error, whatever it is, in 30 days elapsed between the 9th of September and the 9th of October. But if at any other time of this year we set our watch when the equation is to be added we must put it so much before the sun as is the equation. But this is plain enough without further illustration.

Of the certainty and exactness of this equation of time, I make a most convincing experiment by an exquisitely rectified pendulum clock, which I bought from Mr. Richard Jarrat, Watchmaker in Lothbury, London, whom I can therefore recommend for his honesty and ability.

And because I have spoken in this chapter of lengthening or shortening of a pendulum, so as to make it go slower or faster so much in a certain time, for doing this generally and not by guess, I have added a table adapted to a pendulum that vibrates seconds, which is supposed to be 39.2 inches long.

Sir Jonas Moore, on page 113 of his *Mathematical Compendium*, gives such a table as this, but whether by the fault of the printer or calculator, it is very erroneous, as anyone may find that will be at the pains to examine it by the following rule for calculating the tables.

The rule is: the lengths of pendulums are to each other reciprocally as the squares of their vibrations in the same time. Thus: if a pendulum 39.2 inches long vibrates 60 times in a minute, how oft will a pendulum 9.8 (viz., one quarter of 39.2) inches long vibrate in a minute? *

So if it be required, how often a pendulum 39 inches will vibrate in a minute, then the analogy will be: $39 : 39.2 :: 3,600 : 3,618$, whose square root is 60.15. That is, a pendulum 39.0 inches long vibrates in a minute 60 times, and 15 hundredths of a vibration more than 60 times. So that by multiplying 15 hundredths of a vibration by 1,440, the number of minutes in 24 hours, we get the number of vibrations which a pendulum 39.0 inches long vibrates in a day more than one of 39.2 inches. And seeing each vibration in a clock adapted for it sends the hand forward a second, by knowing the number of vibrations which a pendulum 39 inches long performs in a day more than a pendulum 39.2 inches long, we may know the number of seconds which it will advance the index of the clock forward more than one 39.2 inches long. By this rule are the following tables calculated.

* This is the half-seconds pendulum. It will vibrate 120 times in a minute. (Author.)

1	2	3	4
38.7	60″.3863	9′.16″.16‴	1′.52″.06‴
38.8	60 .3084	7 .24 .10	1 .51 .40
38.9	60 .2309	5 .32 .30	1 .51 .20
39.0	60 .1536	3 .41 .10	1 .50 .40
39.1	60 .0766	1 .50 .20	1 .50 .20
39.2	60 .0000	0 .00 .00	
39.3	59 .9236	1 .50 .00	1 .50 .00
39.4	59 .8475	3 .39 .36	1 .49 .36
39.5	59 .7717	5 .28 .45	1 .49 .09
39.6	59 .6962	7 .17 .30	1 .48 .45
39.7	59 .6210	9 .05 .45	1 .48 .15

The first column has in the middle the length of the Pendulum 39.2; upwards it diminisheth one tenth, and downward it increaseth one tenth. The second Column is the vibrations and parts of a vibration performed in a minute by the lengths in the first. The third Column is the minutes and seconds that these lengthenings and shortenings of the Pendulum will cause in a day, and are gotten by multiplying 1440′ the minutes in a day by the Decimals above or under 60″. The 4th and last Column are the differences of the 3rd. The like Table may be made to any length of a Pendulum, respect being had to the foregoing Rule.

Johannes Kelpius

AFTER·PAINTING·FROM·LIFE·BY·DR·CHRISTOPHER·WITT·1706

The first oil painting made in the Colonies showed a clock. Christopher Witt, clockmaker and all-around man of learning, is credited with having made the first oil painting in the Colonies. In 1706 he portrayed Johannes Kelpius, the *Magister* of the Pietists. In this painting he showed a clock in the background, and it is safe to assume that this timepiece was made by Witt himself. The original painting is owned by the Historical Society of Pennsylvania. The drawing here shown was made from the original painting some years back by John R. Sinnock, one-time chief engraver of the United States Mint in Philadelphia and an artist of world-wide reputation. Among many other works, he designed the now famous Purple Heart Medal. (*Courtesy of Henry S. Borneman.*)

RIGHT: The dial of Ahaz. "Behold, I will bring again the shadow of the degrees, which is gone down in the sun dial of Ahaz, ten degrees backward" (Isaiah 38: 8). One of the most interesting mementos of horology in early Pennsylvania is the Dial of Ahaz. This instrument at one time belonged to Johannes Kelpius, *Magister* of the Pietists. It was made by Christopher Schissler, a famed instrument maker of Germany, in 1578. The fact that this rather complicated and accurately made instrument was brought to Pennsylvania before 1700 is an indication of the state of learning among some of the inhabitants. Engraved upon the base of the instrument is a Latin inscription which, translated, reads: "This semicircular shell explains the miracle of the 38th chapter of Isaiah. For if you will fill the basin with water, the shadow of the sun is borne backwards ten degrees. Moreover, it indicates any common hour together with that of the planets which they call hours." (*Courtesy The American Philosophical Society, Philadelphia.*)

LEFT AND RIGHT BELOW: The oldest pendulum-controlled clock in existence. This clock was made by Salomon Coster in 1657 at The Hague under Christiaan Huygens's personal supervision. It is the oldest pendulum clock known. (*Courtesy National Museum of the History of Science, Leiden, the Netherlands.*)

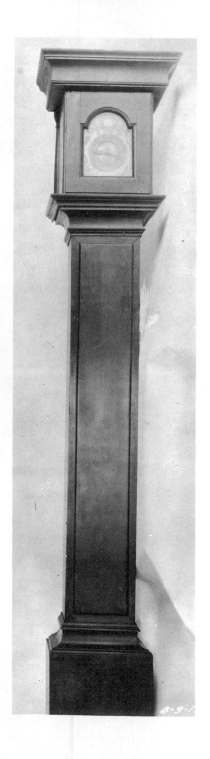

The case of James Logan's clock. James Logan (1674–1751) was the man who really made Philadelphia a city of natural philosophers, inventors, botanists, and experimental scientists. He set the stage for the coming of Franklin. Born in the north of Ireland in 1674, he was forced to flee with his family to England in about 1690 because of the civil wars. They first went to London but later settled in Bristol. Here he attracted the attention of William Penn and accompanied him on his second visit to Pennsylvania late in 1699. The fifty-two years which James Logan spent in Pennsylvania were full of honors—he was President of the Assembly and Chief Justice. His achievements were many, and he built up the greatest private collection of books in the Colonies. A careful search has never disclosed a clock owned by James Logan, although he resided at "Stenton"—his estate— where most of the learned men of the times came to visit him. In the collection in the Independence Hall group in Philadelphia has been found a most unusual clock case—58 inches high —of the type common in England in the latter seventeenth century. A search of the records disclosed that this case was presented to the City of Philadelphia, then owner of the State House, in 1877. The donor, Harrison Whitman of Germantown, stated that it was the case of James Logan's clock, which well it might be. The works are missing but the case has been furnished with a "false" dial upon which is inscribed "I. L.," evidently for James Logan, and the date 1690. This dial and the date were obviously the work of a later hand, but there can be little doubt about the authenticity of the case. (*Courtesy National Park Service, U. S. Department of the Interior.*)

Samuel Bispham clock, c. 1695.
The oldest Pennsylvania tall
case clock known, it is still in
original condition. From private collection of Vincent D.
Andrus.

William Martin,
Bristol,
c. 1695.

Johannes
Fromanteel,
London,
c. 1665.

Christopher Sauer,
Pennsylvania,
c. 1735.

The three clocks of The Library Company. The pendulum
clock travels from Holland to England to Pennsylvania.

A spring dial by Thomas Wagstaffe, London, 1764. "Esteemed Friends. — The Regard I bear the Province of Pennsilvania, Respect to the City of Philadelphia in particular & Esteem for its Inhabitants. The Distinguishing marks of the Favours I have received from them Claim my acknowledgements and as a small Token thereof Present them with a Spring Dial for the use of the Pennsilvania Hospital to be fixed up therein at the Direction of the Managers. In the Performance whereof I have not so much Consulted Ornament & Elegance as real Usefulness being executed in the best Manner for Keeping Time. I request your acceptance thereof and am with Real Esteem Your Assured Fr'd, THOS. WAGSTAFFE. London the 16th 8th mo. 1764."

This clock was duly received in Philadelphia, "Per the ship *Hannover*, Capt. Falkner." It is still a cherished possession of the Pennsylvania Hospital, which was founded in 1751, the oldest hospital in the United States. Before its foundation there were no institutions in any of the Colonies devoted solely to the care of injured and sick persons. Thomas Wagstaffe was well known in London as a clockmaker and Quaker. Most Quakers, when visiting London, called upon him and not a few bought clocks. There seems to be some indication that Thomas Wagstaffe owned land at one time in Pennsylvania but whether or not he ever visited the Province has not been ascertained. The clock is circular, 81 inches in diameter. It is still running and may be seen at The Pennsylvania Hospital. (*Courtesy The Pennsylvania Hospital, Philadelphia.*)

"A clock sent thither by the Royal Society." Astronomical Regulator made by John Shelton, London, for the Royal Society, 1760. "John Shelton's astronomical regulator is the symbol of an era two centuries ago when geodetic and geophysical inquiry was first reaching from London to the far corners of the earth and was linking these corners together. A swinging pendulum of constant length linked Greenwich to St. Helena, to the Cape of Good Hope, to Barbadoes, to southeastern Pennsylvania, to Tahiti, and many other regions. The surface of the earth includes them all. What is the shape of this surface?" Thomas D. Cope, University of Pennsylvania.

RIGHT: This clock, still keeping time in the rooms of the Royal Society in London, is a symbol of the close ties between the scientific life of England and that of Pennsylvania—it need only be mentioned that Benjamin Franklin was a member of the Royal Society and the founder of the American Philosophical Society. This clock is also a memento of the work of Mason and Dixon at the forks of the Brandywine in Chester County. Few boundaries in America are today better known than the Mason and Dixon Line, the traditional geographical division between North and South. Charles Mason and Jeremiah Dixon were in the American Colonies from the autumn of 1763 to the autumn of 1768, surveying and marking the boundary between Maryland and the three lower counties of Pennsylvania. They set up their headquarters at the farm of John Harlan, in Chester County, and among other things measured a degree of latitude. For this work the Royal Society "sent thither" the regulator made by John Shelton.

Few clocks have traveled farther and served science better than this one. Great preparations were made for the observation of the transit of Venus across the sun scheduled for June 5, 1761. From these observations, made in all parts of the world, it would be possible to make a better determination of the sun's distance from the earth. At a meeting in July 1760, the Royal Society resolved to buy a clock to be used at St. Helena by the Rev. Nevil Maskelyne (who became Astronomer Royal in 1765). This clock was made by John Shelton. Its subsequent history is fascinating:

1761. Used by Maskelyne for observations of the transit of Venus at St. Helena, June 5, 1761. Maskelyne then sent the clock to

the Cape of Good Hope, where Jeremiah Dixon, who had observed the transit there, was also to observe the difference of the force of gravity between the two places. It was returned to London in 1762.

1764. H.M.S. *Tartar* sailed from the Nore to the Barbadoes, carrying the clock for the purpose of checking Harrison's No. 4 Chronometer.

1766. In October 1765, Mason and Dixon wrote the Royal Society, proposing that while in America they measure a degree of longitude and a degree of latitude. The Shelton clock was sent them on the *Ellis*, commanded by Captain Samuel Richardson Egdon, who sailed in December. The ship was wrecked, but the clock damage was confined to a broken suspension spring, which was repaired. The Society ordered the clock returned and it was back in England in November 1767.

1768. The clock was sent to King George's Island (Tahiti) in care of Charles Green in the *Endeavour*, commanded by Captain Cook, to observe another transit of Venus. It returned safely.

1774. The Council of the Royal Society selected the mountain of Schichallion in Scotland to determine the density of the earth. The Shelton clock was used on this expedition.

1819. Finally the clock accompanied Lieut. W. E. Parry on his expedition into the Arctic in search for the Northwest Passage.

NOTE 1: The earth is not a perfect sphere; it is flattened at the poles. The distance from the center of the earth to the surface at sea level is greatest at the equator. For this reason a clock pendulum of such length that it will make 86,535 vibrations in a mean solar day in London will make only 86,400 at the equator in the same period, because the pull or force of gravity in the latter position is less than at the former; a simple calculation shows how much. The same is true of any two places on the earth's surface.

NOTE 2: John Shelton was born at Clerkenwell, London, in 1702. He was apprenticed to Henry Stanbury in 1712 for seven years. When free of his apprenticeship he joined the Clockmakers' Company, being admitted to the Livery on July 16, 1766. He worked for George Graham for many years. Shelton made many fine astronomical regulators but seems not to have prospered financially, because in 1777 the president of the Royal Society presented to the Board of Longitude a petition by John Shelton praying for relief since he, his wife, and family were destitute.

NOTE 3: Regarding the clock's arrival at St. Helena, Maskelyne wrote: "The pendulum had not been taken off the clock for carriage, but was secured to the clock case, in order to prevent it from receiving any damage. A piece of wood was secured to the back of the clock case, having a round cavity in it, just large enough to receive the bob of the pendulum; another piece of wood, with such another cavity in it, likewise fitting the bob of the pendulum, was applied to it, on the forepart, and secured firmly to the other piece and to the back of the clock case. Two little pieces of wood likewise kept the upper part of the pendulum in its place from receiving any motion near the centre of suspension. When the pieces of wood were taken away and the pendulum thereby disengaged, the clock was fit for use; only to adjust the pendulum to the same exact length, as it was set at Greenwich, a mark had been made on the rod, where the top of the pendulum rose to: and Dr. Bradley informed me of the number, which stood against the index, on the bottom of the pendulum, by screwing, or unscrewing which, the bob is elevated or depressed."

"Clock Shewing the Hours, Minutes, and Seconds, having only three Wheels, and two Pinions in the Whole Movement. Invented by Dr. Franklin of Philadelphia." Many books on clocks have shown the now-famous Franklin three-wheel clock in diagrammatic form with little or no explanation. This clock is probably best known through James Ferguson, the great self-taught British scientist, who mentioned it and suggested improvements in his *Select Exercises* published in 1773. The question "Why a three-wheel clock?" is best answered by Ferguson's own words: "The simpler that any machine is, the better it will be allowed to be, by every man of science." It is also stated that several clocks were made according to this ingenious plan. The mechanism of the clock was indeed simple, but telling time by it was not. The outer circle of the clock, shown in Figure 1 (in diagram LOWER RIGHT) was divided into quadrants, each representing an hour. Each quadrant, in turn, was divided into 60 minutes of time. The hand A made one complete revolution in four hours. The hours were engraved on spiral spaces as shown. Thus, the time as it appears on the drawing, for instance, was either 32½ minutes past XII, or past IIII, or past VIII, and so on. The small hand B in the arch at the top went around once in a minute and showed seconds. The thought was that one could hardly be four hours off in estimating the time, therefore the true hour and minute could be ascertained from the clock. Figure 2 shows the wheel-work plan of the clock. The great wheel A revolves once in four hours and has 160 teeth. The "hour hand" is attached to the axis of this great wheel. The great wheel A turns the pinion B (ten leaves) and therefore B makes one revolution in one sixteenth of four hours, or in a quarter of an hour. On the axis of the pinion B is attached the wheel C, having 120 teeth. The wheel C revolves once in a quarter of an hour and drives the pinion D (eight leaves). Therefore D revolves once in one minute. The "second" hand is attached to the axis of D and revolves once in a minute. Also attached to the axis of D is the common wheel E, having 30 teeth. This is the escape wheel and is attached to a seconds pendulum, as in a "common clock." That the basic principle of the Franklin three-wheel clock was sound is proved by the fact that very recently Mr. P. H. Breakwell made a facsimile from the description found in Ferguson's book and the clock worked perfectly (UPPER RIGHT).

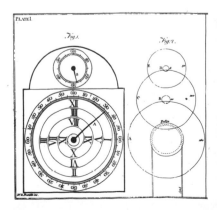

LEFT: The maker of the first State House clock in Philadelphia, Thomas Stretch (died 1765). It was Thomas Stretch who made the first State House clock in Philadelphia, not his father, Peter Stretch, as is so often stated erroneously. The father died in 1746 and the clock was not made until 1753. Thomas Stretch was a prominent citizen of his time. He was a founder and the first governor of the Schuylkill Fishing Company. This was founded in 1732 and is now the oldest club in the world in continuous existence. The name was changed to The State in Schuylkill in 1781. This clockmaker served as governor of the club from the time of its founding until his death.

RIGHT: Peter Stretch clock (c. 1740). This clock belongs to the Schuylkill Fishing Company. The clock here shown, made by Peter Stretch, father of Thomas Stretch, was presented to the fishing club some eighty years ago.

RIGHT: David Rittenhouse (1732–1796), painted by John Trumbull. (*Pennsylvania Academy
of the Fine Arts, Philadelphia.*) David Rittenhouse, at the age of nineteen, opened a clockmaking shop at the family farm in Norriton.
He worked and studied, seriously impairing
his health. Then he went to Yellow Springs,
Pennsylvania, for his health, but soon returned
with a permanent pain in his breast. In 1766
he married Eleanor Colston, a Quakeress and
daughter of a neighboring farmer. He moved
to Philadelphia in 1770, where he suffered the
loss of his wife, a great blow to him. In 1772
he was painted by Charles Willson Peale, the
same year in which he married Hannah Jacobs.
Rittenhouse had a very active time during the
Revolution, dividing his time between science
and the public offices which were thrust upon
him. He grew old and feeble, and the troublesome pain in his breast had chiseled its way
into his delicate and sensitive features.

LEFT: The Rittenhouse clock now in the possession of the Drexel
Institute of Technology, Philadelphia, was perhaps second only
to the orreries as the greatest effort of David Rittenhouse. While
this clock is well known, its importance can hardly be overem-
phasized. The case, over nine feet high, two feet wide, and fifteen
inches deep, is a superb example of 18th-century Philadelphia
cabinet work. Its mechanism includes a musical attachment with
sixteen sets of chimes. An accurate planetarium is placed upon the
face above the dial plate. The flight of time is recorded in seconds,
minutes, hours, and days, and the position of the moon and stars
is likewise indicated. It is peculiar to David Rittenhouse clocks
that each one has a pedigree. Presented to the Drexel Institute in
1898 by Mrs. George W. Childs, widow of the publisher, this
clock was constructed originally for Joseph Potts, who was to
have paid $640 for it. However, in the spring of 1774, it was pur-
chased by Thomas Prior, who during the British occupation of
Philadelphia refused General Sir William Howe's offer of 120
guineas for it, as well as an offer of $800 from the Spanish Min-
ister. After Prior's death in 1801 the clock became the property
of Professor Barton, biographer of David Rittenhouse. From him
the ownership passed to James Swain, at the sale of whose effects
in October 1879 it was purchased by George W. Childs. Joseph
Potts, the man for whom the clock was originally made, was a
colonial forge owner and a man of wealth and consequence—but
at the same time shrewd, frugal, and of simple tastes. Having
ordered a timepiece from David Rittenhouse, he was offered this
clock but decided it was far too elaborate and expensive. Rittenhouse thereupon compromised by making Potts a "half clock,"
the only wall clock he is known to have made.

The Rittenhouse clock of The Pennsylvania Hospital. Second only to the masterpiece in the Drexel Institute of Technology, in Philadelphia, is the Rittenhouse clock in the Pennsylvania Hospital. Since the planetarium on this clock shows the planet Uranus, which was not discovered until 1781 by the astronomer Frederick William Herschel, the clock must have been made after that date. Unfortunately the clock was at one time "extensively" repaired by another Philadelphia clockmaker, J. L. Groppengiesser. There is extant a rather confusing account of the cause for these repairs—the breaking of a cord and the consequent dropping of a weight, damaging the mechanism which "then occupied the lower part of the case." This description would better fit the clock shown on page 143.

The upper central portion, above the dial, exhibits the planetarium, which shows the motion of the planets Uranus, Jupiter, Saturn, Mars, Venus, and the earth. In the upper left-hand corner of the dial proper is a smaller dial giving the position of the moon. In the upper right-hand corner is a dial showing the difference between mean and apparent time. In the lower left-hand corner is a device for controlling the striking mechanism, and in the lower right-hand corner is a dial indicating the succession of the six tunes played by the clock. On the inner hour circle of the dial is a representation of the phases of the moon. This also shows the movement of the earth independent of the moon. The clock has two chiming bells sounding the quarter hours and ten musical bells playing a tune each hour. When the clock was repaired by Groppengiesser, he put in a new music barrel playing "Old Folks at Home," "Home, Sweet Home," "Auld Lang Syne," "The Star Spangled Banner," "The Last Rose of Summer," and "Then You'll Remember Me." It is not known what tunes the clock originally played. The clock requires winding only once every thirty days. When first made, this clock cost more than one thousand dollars. It was deposited in the Hospital by Miss Sarah Zane in 1819 and became its property, through her will, when she died in 1870. (*Courtesy The Pennsylvania Hospital.*)

ABOVE: The orrery made by David Rittenhouse for the College of New Jersey (Princeton University) in 1771. This orrery has recently been restored and is now in the Princeton Library.

LEFT: An important but little-known Rittenhouse item. One of the most unusual clocks in the United States today is all but unknown. There is evidence that it was in the home of David Rittenhouse at the time of his death, and while not marked with his name, it is presumed that he made it for his own use. For many years this clock was on loan exhibition in Memorial Hall, Fairmount Park, Philadelphia, but was eventually sold by the estate of its owners. The clock is provided with an elaborate planetarium worked out with a high degree of scientific skill. The unique feature of this planetarium is that it is placed in the upper part of the front panel of the body *beneath* the hood and works. It is most interesting to compare this clock with the Pennsylvania Hospital Rittenhouse clock. In the latter, the planetarium is placed in the arch above the dial, as might be expected. Probably no clock today offers a greater challenge in research and restoration than does this one, and it is to be hoped that it will eventually find a permanent home in a museum. (*Courtesy Joe Kindig, Jr., York, Pennsylvania.*)

UPPER LEFT: Handsome tall case clock made by Valentin Urletig, the master of Reading, Berks County, Pennsylvania. This maker was working in Reading as early as 1758 and was well known for the excellence of his workmanship. (*Courtesy E. S. Rhoads, Birdsboro, Pennsylvania.*)

UPPER RIGHT: Robert Shearman clock (c. 1800; *Philadelphia Museum of Art*). An excellent example of a Philadelphia clock of about 1800. This clock, it will be noticed, has a white dial with painted floral sprays in the spandrels. Maker's name on the dial, "R. Shearman, Philadelphia." The mahogany case is in the Chippendale style. It has upright front with quarter-round pilasters and domed door, arched hood with scroll pediments supported by detached column on each side of hood, three urn and flame finials with fluted block under second urn. Robert Shearman was in business in Wilmington, Delaware, as early as 1768. He was in Philadelphia from 1799 to 1804.

LOWER LEFT: George Faber clock (late 18th century; *Philadelphia Museum of Art*). George Faber, Sumneytown (sometimes spelled "Sunnytown" on his clocks), Montgomery County, was making clocks in 1773 and probably before. In 1773 he moved to Reading, some thirty miles away, and worked there for several years. This is an early example of painted dial decorated with figures at each corner. Lower right and left show Youth and Age. The mahogany case is interesting—paneled door and columns—scroll hood. The hood is ornamented with small columns at four corners —scrolled and voluted top, with rosette terminations. In center, turned finial, below which is winged face carved in low relief, possibly representing the moon. Two ornamental flames rising from square pedestals at the corners.

LOWER RIGHT: William Huston clock (c. 1770; *Philadelphia Museum of Art*). This clock is particularly interesting because of its very fine case, the maker of which is known. It is a mahogany case with quarter-column corners. The hood is scrolled—the inner ends of the scrolls being finished into rosettes. Urn and flame finials. Pierced border above dial. Bracket feet. Dial domed. Case maker's label inside case. Also "E. J." branded in the wood five times. Case made by Edward James.

FAR RIGHT: John J. Parry clock (early 19th century), Philadelphia. (*Collection of Mr. A. C. Scott, Grosse Point, Michigan.*) John J. Parry (1773–1835) was a nephew of David Rittenhouse's second wife (Hannah Jacobs), and upon the death of David Rittenhouse in 1796 inherited the great clockmaker's tools. Parry was in business in Philadelphia from 1794 until his death in 1835. This clock is a fine example of post-Revolutionary clockmaking in Philadelphia. The dial is painted.

RIGHT: Francis Richardson clock (c. 1725; *Philadelphia Museum of Art, Philadelphia*). Inscribed on dial: "Francis Richardson, Philada Fecit." Walnut case, flat molded top, brass columns at corners, brass dial. Francis Richardson (1681–1729) was born in New York but came to Philadelphia, where he established himself as a silversmith and clockmaker. He was the father of Joseph Richardson (1711–1784), also a clockmaker and silversmith.

LOWER RIGHT: Tall case clock by John Wood, Jr., of Philadelphia. John Wood advertised extensively in English and German newspapers between 1760 and 1793. He was successful as a clockmaker and merchant. (*Courtesy Dr. and Mrs. William S. Magee, Philadelphia.*)

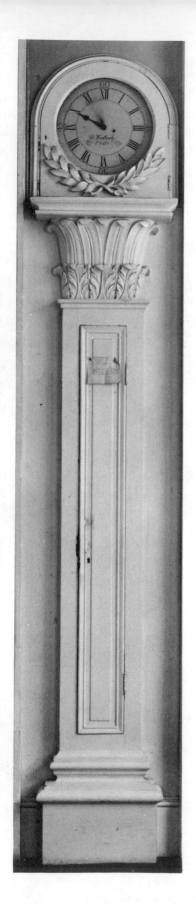

LEFT: A most unusual clock in the Mayor's office in the Old City Hall, Philadelphia. After the Revolution it was decided to add to the State House group of buildings. The building at Sixth and Chestnut Streets was built for the County offices. This building was occupied by the Senate and House of Representatives until the capital was moved permanently to Washington; it is now known as Congress Hall. The building at Fifth and Chestnut Streets was built for the City offices, including that of the mayor. It was finished in 1789. The clock shown in the photograph was purchased in London, England, in 1789 and brought to Philadelphia for the mayor's private office. The original casing of the clock was let into the wall and it has remained in this position ever since. The clock is about nine feet tall. This clock was completely rebuilt by a Philadelphia maker, David Weatherly, in 1830, and bears his name on the dial. (*Courtesy National Park Service, U. S. Department of the Interior.*)

UPPER RIGHT, OPPOSITE: A Pennsylvania clock in Utah. The deep affection held by Pennsylvanians for their tall case clocks is shown by an exhibit enshrined in the museum of the Daughters of the Utah Pioneers in Salt Lake City. This exhibit, a clock made in Chester County, Pennsylvania, is a symbol of the memories of their former homes that the pioneers carried westward with them. The clock was made in about 1794 and became the property of Jacob Baum of Downingtown, Chester County, Pennsylvania. Few clocks in America have had a more romantic history.

In the spring of 1829 a group of Mormons moved together in a settlement in Chester County. Joseph Smith, the prophet, visited them and preached there. Jacob Baum was one of the group and became a friend of the founder. A large number of these people followed Joseph Smith to Nauvoo in the early 1840s. Jacob Baum was in Nauvoo as early as 1843, and in 1851 he was a speaker at a conference held at Kanesville, Iowa (now Council Bluffs). The Baum family arrived in Salt Lake City in the fall of 1852. Jacob Baum had a daughter, Elizabeth, who was born in Brandywine Township, Chester County, in 1834; she married George Washington Bean in Provo, Utah, in 1853. She died in Ephraim, Utah, in 1916 and the following year her family presented the clock to the museum.

This clock was carried from Chester County, Pennsylvania, to Nauvoo and then through the great Mormon overland migration to Council Bluffs and Salt Lake City. The name of the clockmaker is not known, but it is a distinct Chester County type. Travel during the migration was by wagon, and space was at a great premium. Somewhere, the body and base of the clock were abandoned and new ones made, evidently upon its arrival in Salt Lake City. (*Courtesy The Central Company, Daughters of the Utah Pioneers, Salt Lake City, Utah.*)

LOWER RIGHT: Pennsylvania watch- and clockmakers turn to building locomotives. There was a very early interest in travel by rail in Pennsylvania. In 1809 Thomas Leiper built a model railway with a wooden track in the Bull's Head Tavern Yard at Third and Callowhill Streets, Philadelphia. Shortly thereafter this same man built a small railroad to haul rock from his quarries on Crum Creek, near Chester, to a dock upon a creek about three quarters of a mile distant. The cars were drawn by oxen; steam locomotives were yet some years away. The famous Rainhill trials in England for steam locomotives aroused international interest. Franklin Peale, proprietor of the Philadelphia Museum, in 1830 approached Matthias W. Baldwin, a watch- and clockmaker who had turned to building machinery, and asked him to build a model locomotive. Baldwin built a small locomotive similar to the "Novelty," which Braithwaite and Ericsson had entered in the Rainhill competition. It is more than possible that Baldwin had only the drawings of the locomotive in the *Journal* of The Franklin Institute to go by. Baldwin was a member of this institution, which had been founded in 1824. On April 25, 1831, the first Baldwin steam locomotive was run at the Peale Museum. So successful was this small locomotive that, early in 1832, The Philadelphia, Germantown & Norristown Railroad Company requested him to build a full-sized locomotive to run on their line. Thus began the great Baldwin Locomotive Works. The announcement of the locomotive at the Peale Museum appeared in Philadelphia newspapers of April 25, 1831, and is interesting in showing the trend of the times. Commerce was beginning to flow between east and west. The time was ripening for the building of railroads, and Baldwin was a pioneer in the construction of American locomotives.

A Matthias Baldwin clock is shown here. (*Courtesy W. M. Smith.*)

ABOVE: Spring power locomotive car (1834). Invented by George W. Duncan, Philadelphia. This quaint drawing is most interesting because it reflects a trend in clockmaking as well as an interest in the building of railroads. George W. Duncan was a hardware merchant, listed in the Directories of Philadelphia from 1830 to 1840. In about 1830 the making of clock springs in America really began to succeed, and undoubtedly Mr. Duncan knew about this. While American industry began to make successful clock springs, his imagination ran forward into giant springs for railway cars. It was in 1831 that Baldwin made his model locomotive for Peale's Museum and in 1832 received his first order for a railway locomotive. This drawing was deposited with The Franklin Institute.

LEFT: Rare Pennsylvania-German clock *Fraktur*. The folk art expressed in this kind of illuminated manuscript had a distinct effect on dial decoration in Pennsylvania. (*Photo courtesy Schwenkfelder Library, Pennsburg, Pa.*)

An unusual Pennsylvania clock of 1949-1950. While it is generally recognized that the making of tall clocks ceased in Pennsylvania by 1850, there are isolated instances of craftsmen working down to the present time. Of particular interest is a fine clock bearing the inscription "Charles L. Yeager, Chambersburg" on the dial. This clock might well confuse the collectors of a later generation.

Harry Amos Metcalfe (1878–1951) made the works of this clock for his friend Charles L. Yeager in 1949–1950. William Lohs, of Jonestown, Pa., painted the dial and put Mr. Yeager's name on it. The works finally came into the possession of David H. Zarger of Chambersburg, Pa., a collector, who had them placed in a fine old case.

Harry Amos Metcalfe was born near Waynesboro, Franklin County, Pa., and as early as ten years of age was working in a machine shop during summers. After finishing grammar school he served his apprenticeship as a machinist. In 1910 he went to work for the Landis Program Clock Co. in Waynesboro and remained with the company until it ceased doing business in 1937. He eventually returned to machine work and when he retired in 1945 he devoted his time to building and repairing clocks.

The works shown are the only complete movement made by Metcalfe during his lifetime. It is much to his credit that he placed a small plate on the back of the movement so that collectors of the future might not be defrauded into thinking this an old clock. This plate reads "Invented and Made by Harry A. Metcalfe, Waynesboro." (*Courtesy David H. Zarger, Chambersburg, Pa.*)

The development of the clock dial: The earliest weight-and-pendulum clocks in tall cases had square dials. The arched dial was introduced about the beginning of the eighteenth century. These three pictures show the development of the use of the semi-circle above the dial proper. They are to be taken as types rather than actual examples of the respective earliest uses of this space. A certain feature may indicate the earliest possible date of a clock, but the same feature may have been used as much as a century or more later by some individual clockmaker.

UPPER LEFT: The cartouche. This shows the earliest use of the semicircle above the dial proper. It was embellished by a cartouche bearing the name of the maker and possibly his place. The cartouche might even carry only a decoration. Such a clock could not be dated before 1700 or thereabouts but might even date as late as the Revolution.

CENTER LEFT: The rocking ship. The second development was the introduction of motion in the semicircle. This dates back to about 1720. These figures, which moved back and forth with the pendulum, took the form of rocking ships, prancing deer, Father Time and his scythe, and a number of other forms. A clock having this feature could not be earlier than about 1720 but the feature is also found in clocks coming down to comparatively recent dates.

LOWER LEFT: Shortly after the introduction of motion in the semicircle above the dial, the moon wheel was conceived. This ingenious arrangement offered a method for telling the phase of the moon at a glance. Thus a very practical and useful, as well as decorative, feature was added. Clocks so equipped cannot be earlier than about 1720–1730, but the moon wheel has persisted in clocks down to the present day. It is found both with early brass dials and later with painted dials.

RIGHT: The moon wheel. This has two full moons painted upon it. Landscape and seascape are opposite each other and between the moons. The rim of the wheel is provided with 118 teeth, 59 for each moon.

BELOW: The dialwork of a clock. The moon's phases, the month, the day of the month, and the day of the week are shown. This illustration from A. Rees' *Cyclopedia, or Universal Dictionary of Arts, Sciences and Literature* (not dated, but Philadelphia c. 1820).

GRAND-FATHER'S CLOCK.

Song and Chorus.

WORDS AND MUSIC BY

HENRY C. WORK.

NEW YORK:

Published by C. M. CADY, 107 Duane St.

To my Sister Lizzie

Grandfather's Clock

Words and Music by HENRY C. WORK
N<u>o</u> 52

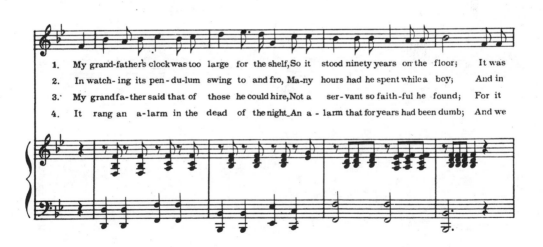

1. My grand-father's clock was too large for the shelf, So it stood ninety years on the floor; It was

2. In watch- ing its pen - du - lum swing to and fro, Ma-ny hours had he spent while a boy; And in

3. My grandfa-ther said that of those he could hire, Not a ser - vant so faith-ful he found; For it

4. It rang an a - larm in the dead of the night_An a - larm that for years had been dumb; And we

tall - er by half than the old man himself, Though it weighed not a pen-ny weight more. It was
childhood and man-hood the clock seemed to know And to share both his grief and his joy. For it
wast-ed no time, and had but one de-sire—At the close of each week to be wound. And it
knew that his spir - it was plum - ing for flight_That his hour of de-parture had come. Still the

bought on the morn of the day that he was born, And was al-ways his treasure and pride; But it
struck twenty-four when he en-tered at the door, With a blooming and beau-ti-ful bride; But it
kept in its place_not a frown up-on its face, And its hands nev-er hung by its side; But it
clock kept the time, with a soft and muffled chime, As we si - lent - ly stood by-his side; But it

stopp'd short nev-er to go a-gain When the old man died.
stopp'd short nev-er to go a-gain When the old man died.
stopp'd short nev-er to go a-gain When the old man died.
stopp'd short nev-er to go a-gain When the old man died.

Chorus

AIR In exact time

Ninety years, without slumbering (tick,tick, tick,tick) His life seconds numbering (tick, tick,tick, tick) It

ALTO

TENOR

Ninety years, without slumbering (tick,tick, tick,tick) His life seconds numbering (tick,tick,tick, tick) It

BASS

stopp'd short never to go a-gain When the old man died.

stopp'd short never to go a-gain When the old man died.

Grandfathers Clock

SEQUEL TO GRAND FATHER'S CLOCK.

SONG AND CHORUS.

WORDS AND MUSIC BY

HENRY C. WORK.

NEW YORK

Published by C. M. CADY, 107 Duane St.

SEQUEL TO

"Grandfather's Clock."

Words and Music by HENRY C. WORK.

Con espressione.

No. 63.

PIANO.

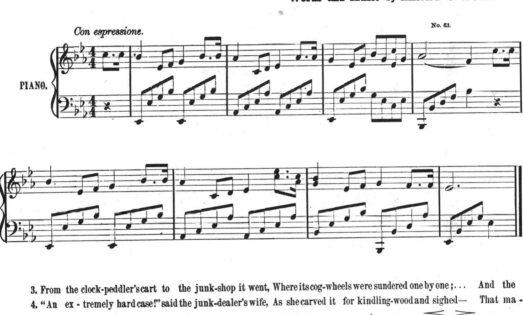

3. From the clock-peddler's cart to the junk-shop it went, Where its cog-wheels were sundered one by one; . . . And the
4. "An ex - tremely hard case!" said the junk-dealer's wife, As she carved it for kindling-wood and sighed— That ma -

1. Once a - gain have I roamed thro' the old-fashioned house, Where my grandfather spent his ninety years, ... There are
2. While we talked of the old clock they all ran it down, Tho' they claimed that it couldn't be made to run. . . . It was

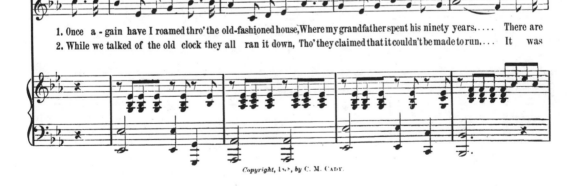

157

brass-found-er joked as they writhed in the flames—"Melt 'em up," says he; "then they will run." There is
hog - a - ny case, with its quaint, figured face, Which so long was my grandfather's pride. "There is

stran-gers in charge, and the change they have wrought—Oh! it sad-dens me, ev-en to tears. Dear old
use - less, they said— it was quite out of style; Built, no doubt, just about the year One. And the

grief in my heart, there are tears in my eyes, Yet in-dig-nant-ly the sight I re-call Of that
hope for the small; there's a chance for us all; For the mighty ones of Time, they must fall!" Says that

clock! when they found you were speechless from grief, Then they went and swapped you off, case and all, For that
words echoed round, with a faint, mocking sound, As if some one gave as-sent to it all: 'Twas that

vain, stuck-up thing (tick, tick, tick, tick, tick, tick, tick, tick), Of that vain, stuck-up thing on the wall.
vain, stuck-up thing (tick, tick, tick, tick, tick, tick, tick, tick), Says that vain, stuck-up thing on the wall.

vain, stuck-up thing (tick, tick, tick, tick, tick, tick, tick, tick), For that vain, stuck-up thing on the wall.
vain, stuck-up thing (tick, tick, tick, tick, tick, tick, tick, tick), 'Twas that vain, stuck-up thing on the wall.

Sequel to Grandfather's Clock.—2.

158

Grand - fa - ther sleeps in his grave: Strange steps resound in the hall!.... And there's that

Grand - fa - ther sleeps in his grave: Strange steps resound in the hall! . .

vain, stuck - up thing (tick, tick, tick, tick, tick, tick, tick, tick), There's that vain, stuck-up thing on the wall.

There's that vain, stuck-up thing on the wall.

Sequel to Grandfather's Clock.—3.

Song & Chorus

GRANDMOTHER'S CLOCK

Words by Jno. F. Cowan

Music by Geo. W. Morgan.

FREE WITH THE NEW YORK
FAMILY STORY PAPER
Nº 260

AN ANNOTATED LIST OF THE CLOCK
AND WATCHMAKERS OF
PHILADELPHIA AND PENNSYLVANIA

1682–1850

A BOOK on clocks and watches is incomplete unless it carries lists of makers. Let us consider the purposes of these lists. First, they serve to aid in the identification and dating of timepieces that fall into the hands of collectors.

But they have a far wider appeal if properly annotated. Ideally, a list should be made up of short biographies of all makers mentioned, giving data on their lives and work. Unfortunately this ideal never can be fully realized. Space would not permit it, and while some men achieved prominence others were obscure and, besides their clocks, left little more than a notation in a tax list or a name in a directory.

All were actors in a great drama; some played major roles, others very minor roles. Just as a playbill lists all who appear, an effort has been made here to list the entire cast. No list of clock- and watchmakers can ever be complete for a town, county, state, or nation. Continued research will always uncover one more. It is very possible that a name mentioned in the lists given herewith will appear on a clock, watch, or watchpaper. Some were makers, others merely dealers, but they all had to do with clocks and watches.

To present these data in a logical, convenient manner, they have been divided into two parts—Philadelphia and Pennsylvania outside of Philadelphia. Pennsylvania began with Philadelphia and expanded outward. As time went on, the spirit of Pennsylvania extended beyond its geographical boundaries and the clocks were carried far and wide. For this reason the lists given here are important not only to Pennsylvanians but to all interested in America and its growth.

Data have been gathered from many sources over a period of years. The directories of Philadelphia have been searched carefully. Some makers remained in one location throughout their entire careers, others were restless and moved about. Some confined their work to clock- and watchmaking—some sought opportunity in other endeavors.

While 1850 has been taken as the date when the tall case clock ceased to be made in Pennsylvania on anything like a large scale, a few instances are given of men who worked on into the second half of the nineteenth century.

CLOCK AND WATCHMAKERS
OF PHILADELPHIA

PHILADELPHIA

PHILADELPHIA was given a charter as a borough by William Penn in 1684. In 1701 the "said town and borough of Philadelphia" was erected into a city.

The original city extended from the Schuylkill on the west to the Delaware River on the east; from Vine Street on the north to Cedar (or South) Street on the south. It covered an area of about two and a quarter square miles. Most of the history of Colonial and Revolutionary times was enacted in the eastern third of the city.

Lines for the county of Philadelphia were established February 1, 1685. Some two hundred towns, villages, and crossroads sprang up in the county surrounding the city. Some had no formal status other than a name, others had their own governments.

Under the Act of February 2, 1854, all these districts, boroughs, and townships were consolidated with the city, and the city and county of Philadelphia occupied the same territory.

Some of these towns, boroughs, and districts in the county were even older than the city itself. Southwark, to the south of the city, was created into a "municipality" by the Assembly in 1762 and fully incorporated in 1794. The district, however, had been settled by the Swedes before the coming of Penn.

Northern Liberties, to the north of the city, took its name from Penn's land policy. All who purchased 500 acres elsewhere in Pennsylvania received a bonus of 2 per cent in acreage in the "liberty lands" outside the city proper. So great was the demand for land in the Northern Liberties that the bonus was cut to eight acres for every 500 purchased.

Germantown was settled in 1683. As early as 1696 Richard Frame wrote of the weaving of linen cloth and papermaking in Germantown.

Aside from Southwark and Northern Liberties, the following "districts" were consolidated with the city in 1854: Kensington, Spring Garden, Moyamensing, Penn (South Penn), Richmond, West Philadelphia, and Belmont.

In addition to Germantown the following "boroughs" were taken into the city; Frankford, Manayunk, Bridesburg, Whitehall, and Aramingo.

Thirteen "townships" were also included: Passayunk, Blockley, Kingsessing, Roxborough, Germantown (there were both a borough and township of this name), Bristol, Oxford, Lower Dublin, Moreland, Unincorporated Northern Liberties, Byberry, Penn (North Penn), and Delaware.

The first Philadelphia City Directories were published in 1785.

Even in these there is a confusion of street names. High Street is referred to as Market Street, as if it were an established name. High Street was not officially changed to Market Street until 1853.

Houses were not numbered until 1790.

Abbreviations:
    C. M.—clockmaker
    W. M.—watchmaker
    C. & W. M.—clock- and watchmaker
    (D)—Directory
    A date in the Directory refers to the year previous. Thus, an

entry in the Directory of 1820 (1820 [D]) indicates that the man was in business at the specified location in 1819.

Since some clock- and watchmakers, during their careers, worked both in Philadelphia and elsewhere in Pennsylvania, in searching for a specific name it may be well to consult both lists.

ANNOTATED LIST

PHILADELPHIA

A

Albright, Thomas F.
c. & w. m.
268 High St. 1843 (D)
246 High St. 1844 (D)–1847 (D)

Amant, Fester
c. & w. m.
150 North Third St. 1794 (D)

Arnold, Jacob
c. m.
9th & Callowhill Sts. 1848 (D)

Ash, Lawrence
c. & w. m.
Advertised 1762–1763. Pennsylvania Gazette, March 25, 1762, "Late from Edward Duffield's." Front St. six doors above Market St.

Attmore, Marshall
c. & w. m.
38 Cedar St. 1821 (D)
S. E. cor. Chestnut & Front 1822 (D)–1824 (D)
55 South Front 1825 (D)–1831 (D)
Market St. below Sixth 1833 (D)
w. m.
Market St. above Tenth
              1835 (D), 1836 (D)
376 Market St. 1837 (D)

Austin, Isaac
c. & w. m.
Advertised as early as 1781. Died 1801.
Cor. Arch & Water Sts. 1785 (D)
7 Mulberry St. 1791 (D)
57 North Water St. 1794 (D)
7 Mulberry (or Arch) St. 1795 (D)
7 Arch St. 1796 (D)–1799 (D)
w. m.
7 Arch St. 1800 (D)–1801 (D)

B

Babcock & Co.
C. Babcock
  jewelry etc.

4 North Third St. 1831 (D)
84 High St. 1833 (D)

Bailey, Banks & Biddle Co.
This firm is still in business at 16th & Chestnut Sts. The business was established Sept. 20, 1832, as Bailey & Kitchen at 136 Chestnut St. This was succeeded by Bailey & Company in 1848. In 1857 Bailey & Company moved to 817 Chestnut St., and in 1869 the firm moved to cor. 12th & Chestnut Sts. Bailey, Banks & Biddle Co. absorbed Bailey & Company in 1878. In 1904 Bailey, Banks & Biddle Co. moved to 1218 Chestnut St. In 1953, firm went to present location. Joseph Trowbridge Bailey, the founder, died in 1854. The record of this firm is as follows:

J. T. Bailey
jeweler
Born 1806, died 1854.
136 Chestnut St. 1839 (D)–1850 (D)

Bailey & Kitchen
jewelers
136 Chestnut St. 1833 (D)–1846 (D)

Bailey & Company
jewelers
136 Chestnut St. 1848 (D)–1850 (D)

Bailey, Gamaliel
w. m.
320 Sassafras St. 1829 (D)–1833 (D)

Bailey, Wm., Jr.
c. & w. m.
120 South Front St. 1816 (D)
151 North Second St. 1817 (D)–1818 (D)
122 North Second St. 1820 (D)–1821 (D)
80 High St. 1822 (D)
This name does not appear again until the directory of 1829 lists it at 80 High St.
80 High St. 1831 (D)
362 High St. 1833 (D)
262 High St. 1835 (D)–1836 (D)

Baily, William
w. m.
A. M. M'Elroy's Directory (1837) lists William Baily at 262 High St.
Desilver's Directory (1837) lists W. Bailey at same address.
357 High St.   1839 (D)–1843 (D)
216 High St.   1844 (D)–1850 (D)

Baker, Benjamin F.
w. m.
192 North Third St.   1825 (D)

Baker, Benjamin H.
c. & w. m.
70 South Third St.   1823 (D), 1824 (D)

Baldwin, Matthias W.
Born Elizabethtown, N. J., Dec. 10, 1795, died Sept. 7, 1866.
Matthias W. Baldwin, the great locomotive builder and founder of the Baldwin Locomotive Works, began as a clockmaker. At the age of 16 he was apprenticed to Woolworth Bros., jewelers, Frankford, Philadelphia. Early in 1817 he entered the establishment of Charles Fletcher, jeweler, 130 Chestnut St., Philadelphia. In 1819 he went into business for himself as a jeweler (and clockmaker) and is listed as follows:
College Avenue   1822 (D)
In the directory of 1823 he is still at 1 College Avenue but is listed as "machinist."

He met David H. Mason, a machinist, and in 1825 went into the business of making book-binding machinery and rolls for printing calico. By 1828 his business had expanded and he moved to Minor St. Needing a steam engine, he made one for himself. He then went into the business of making steam engines. In 1831 Baldwin made a model of a steam locomotive after plans by Ericsson for Franklin Peale, and this small engine ran around a track in Peale's Museum. Early in 1832 he received an order from the Philadelphia & Germantown Railroad for a locomotive, and the rest of his life was devoted to locomotive building.

Banks, Joseph
w. m.
Grissel's Alley   1819 (D), 1820 (D)

Banstein, John
c. m.
131 St. John's St., Northern Liberties
1791 (D)

Barbeck, C. G.
w. m.
Cedar near Vernon St.
1835 (D), 1836 (D)

Barber, James
clocks & clock dealer
238 High St.   1842 (D)–1850 (D)

Barnhill, Robert
w. m.
Advertised in Penna. Evening Post, March 20, 1777

Barrow, Samuel
c. & w. m.
Set up clock- and watchmaking shop in Chestnut St. between Front and Second in Oct. 1771. Barrow advertised that he had recently come from London.

Bassett, Geo. Francis
c. & w. m.
131 South Front St.   1797 (D)

Bassett, John Francis
c. & w. m.
131 South Front St.   1798 (D)

Bayley, Simeon C.
w. m.
83 Elm St.   1794 (D)

Beigel, Henry
c. m.
11th & George Sts.   1816 (D), 1817 (D)

Belk, William
w. & c. m.
76 South Front St.   1797 (D)
w. m.
76 South Front St.   1798 (D), 1799 (D)

Bell, William
c. & w. m.
21 South Front St.   1805 (D)

Bennett, Alfred
w. m. & jeweler
169 Cherry St.   1837 (D)

Berrgant, Peter
c. m.
Germantown Road below Master St.
1829 (D)–1833 (D).

Biddle, Owen
clockmaker, scientist and statesman.
Born 1737, died 1799. Advertised from
1764 to 1770. For full life of Owen Biddle
see Pennsylvania Magazine of History and
Biography, Volume 16, page 299.

Biegel, Henry W.
c. m.
191 North Third St.   1810 (D), 1811 (D)
c. & w. m.
190 North Third St.   1813 (D)

Biernsen, Thomas (also listed as Thormod)
c. & w. m.
49 South Tenth St.   1839 (D)–1842 (D)

Billon, Charles
c. & w. m. & jeweler
45 South Third St.   1798 (D)–1801 (D)
w. m.
69 South Second St.   1801 (D)–1803 (D)
w. m. & jeweler
173 High St.   1804 (D), 1805 (D)
75 South Second St.   1806 (D)–1811 (D)
81 South Second St.   1813 (D)–1818 (D)
146 Race St.   1819 (D), 1820 (D)

Billon, Charles & Company
watchmakers
12 South Third St.   1795 (D)–1797 (D)

Birnie, Lawrence
w. m.
Opened a shop in lodgings in Arch St.
near Second in Oct. 1774. Advertised in
1775 and in 1777 was located in Second
St., five doors below Arch. He was advanced 300 pounds by the Committee of
Safety in 1776 to erect an air furnace and
mill for file cutting in connection with a
gun lock factory.

Bispham, Samuel
c. m.
This man was working in Philadelphia as
early as 1696. While little is known about
him, a clock he made is still in practically
its original condition, there having been
little restoration or change in either case

or works. This clock may well be the earliest Pennsylvania clock extant in anything
like its original case.

Black, John
w. m.
64 Cedar St.   1846 (D)–1849 (D)

Blatt, John
clock dealer
651 North Second St.   1841 (D)
582 North Third St.   1842 (D)

Bode, William
w. m.
10 Market St.   1796 (D)
228 North Second St.   1797 (D)
c. & w. m.
426 North Front St.   1797 (D)

Bond, William
clock dial manufacturer
159 Moyamensing Road
1829 (D)–1833 (D)

Bonnaud, "Mr."
w. m.
62 Race St.   1799 (D)

Boss, James
watchcase maker
Invented and patented gold-filled watchcase, 1859. Factory was at N.E. cor. Fifth
and Chestnut Sts.

Bower, Michael
c. m.
75 North Second St.   1799 (D)

Boyd, Thomas
w. m.
41 Callowhill St.   1807 (D), 1808 (D)
315 North Front St.   1809 (D)

Bradier, John
w. m.
40 Coates St.   1802 (D)–1805 (D)

Brant (Brandt), Brown & Lewis
watchmakers
158 North Second St.   1795 (D)

Brandt & Mathey
c. & w. m.
In Oct. 1795, Brandt and Matthey, "watch-

and clockmakers from Switzerland," advertised at 158 North Second St., "corner of New (St.)."
158 North Second St.   1797 (D)–1799 (D)

Brandt, Aime & Charles
c. & w. m.
129 North Second St.   1800 (D)–1814 (D)

Brandt, Aime
w. m. & jeweler
129 North Second St.   1816 (D)–1824 (D)
c. & w. m.
129 North Second St.   1825 (D)–1831 (D)

Brandt, Charles & Co.
jewelers
12 North Second St.   1816 (D), 1817 (D)

Brazier, Amable
French watchmaker & jeweler
7 North Third St.   1794 (D)–1796 (D)
23 North Third St.   1797 (D)–1811 (D)
12 South Third St.   1813 (D)–1825 (D)
108 South Fourth St.   1828 (D), 1829 (D)
117 South Third St.   1831 (D)–1833 (D)

Brearly, James
(also spelled Brearley)
c. & w. m.
67 Mulberry (or Arch) St.
                    1795 (D), 1796 (D)
79 North Second St.   1797 (D), 1798 (D)
77 North Second St.   1799 (D)
75 North Second St.   1801 (D)–1803 (D)
25 North Second St.   1804 (D), 1805 (D)
78 North Third St.   1806 (D)–1811 (D)
113½ North Third St.   1813 (D)
w. m.
Old York Road below Germantown Road
                    1814 (D)
115 North Third St.   1816 (D)–1822 (D)

Brewer, William
Advertised in Sept. 1774, opening shop in Chestnut St. between Front and Second for the making and mending of clocks and watches.
w. m.
55 Walnut St.   1791 (D)
Friends' Alms House   1803 (D), 1804 (D)
c. & w. m.
Friends' Alms House, Walnut St.
                    1814 (D)–1822 (D)
4 Friends' Alms House   1823 (D), 1824 (D)

5 Friends' Alms House   1825 (D)
Note: Isaac Brewer is listed at Friends' Alms House as watchmaker in Directory of 1813, but this is evidently a mistake in the first name.

Brown, John
c. & w. m.
359 North Second St.   1819 (D)–1822 (D)

Burk, Charles
w. m.
Front St. above Phoenix   1848 (D)

Burkhart, Trudpert
musical clockmaker
24 Willow St.   1839 (D)
168 North Fourth St.   1841 (D)–1843 (D)
310 Callowhill St.   1844 (D), 1845 (D)
2 Ridgeway's Court   1846 (D)

Burkloe, Samuel
w. m.
13 Shippen St.   Southwark   1791 (D)
Shippen St. near Vernon   1796 (D)
Corner Shippen and Vernon Sts.   1797 (D)
13 Shippen St.   1799 (D)–1813 (D)

Burns, Hugh
c. & w. m.
94 Cherry St.   1809 (D)
94 Chestnut St.   1810 (D), 1811 (D)

C

Calderwood, Andrew
w. & c. m.
22 Strawberry Alley   1800 (D)
22 Strawberry St.   1801 (D)–1807 (D)
near First Gate on Germantown Road
                    1809 (D)–1817 (D)
Germantown Road above First Gate
                    1818 (D)–1822 (D)

Caldwell, J. E. & Co.
This firm is still in business at Juniper & Chestnut Sts. James Emott Caldwell, the founder, came to Philadelphia in 1836 and started in business selling watches and clocks. In 1839 the business moved to 163 Chestnut St., the firm name being then Bennett & Caldwell. In 1844 the business moved to 140 Chestnut St., where it remained until 1858. In 1848 the name was changed to James E. Caldwell & Co. From

1858 to 1868 the address was 822 Chestnut St. From 1868 to 1916 the address was 902 Chestnut St. In 1916 the firm moved to its present address, Juniper and Chestnut Sts.

Campbell, Charles
c. & w. m.
3 South Fourth St.   1794 (D)–1798 (D)
55 South Front St.   1799 (D)–1803 (D)
Charles Campbell advertised extensively. In July 1798 he advertised astronomical and musical clocks for sale. In November 1798 he moved to the shop formerly occupied by John Wood, 55 South Front St. (corner Front & Chestnut).

Cannon, William
Died 1753.
Worked in Philadelphia in the 1720s, thus being one of the earliest clockmakers in the city. Later moved to Burlington, N. J., where he died. Joseph Hollinshead, the great New Jersey clockmaker, was administrator of his estate.

Capper, Michael
w. m.
99 Race St.   1798 (D)
119 Race St.   1799 (D), 1800 (D)

Carrel, John
clock- & watchmaker & ironmonger
Advertised Sept. 1787 as having eight-day clocks, japanned clock faces, and tools for sale at Front St., six doors below Market. In Sept. 1791 he advertised ironmongery, cutlery and saddlery, as well as clocks, at 32 Market St., corner Letitia St.
He advertised as late as Jan. 1796.
32 High St.   1791 (D)

Carrel, John & Daniel
w. & c. m.
Front St. between Market & Chestnut
                              1785 (D)

Carter, Jacob
w. m.
21 North Alley   1806 (D)–1808 (D)

Carter, Thomas
w. m.
N. W. cor. Swanson & Parkham's Alley
                      1823 (D), 1824 (D)

Carter, William
w. m.
This man carried on trade of watchmaker and repairer in Philadelphia a year after Penn founded the city. Died in 1738.

Carver, Jacob
c. & w. m.
Front corner of Arch St.   1785 (D)
55 Mulberry St.   1791 (D)
73 Mulberry St.   1793 (D)
In May 1793 Jacob Carver advertised that he was carrying on watchmaking business at the same address as Griffith Owen, 73 Mulberry St.
44 South Front St.   1794 (D)–1798 (D)
51 South Front St.   1799 (D)
76 South Front St.   1800 (D)
13 North Front St.   1801 (D)–1804 (D)
4 North Second St.   1808 (D)
76 Sassafras St.   1811 (D)
126 St. John St.   1825 (D)–1833 (D)

Castan, Stephen
watchcase maker
43 Union St.   1818 (D)

Castan, Stephen & Co.
w. m. & jewelers
53 South Third St.   1819 (D), 1820 (D)

Cecil, Charles
clocksmith
105 Walnut St. (near)   1808 (D)–1811 (D)
In 1810 Charles Cecil is listed as a locksmith.

Chandlee, Benjamin
c. m.
Born in Ireland in 1685. Came to Philadelphia and was apprenticed to Abel Cottey to learn "the art and mystery of clockmaking." In 1710 he married Sarah, the daughter of Abel Cottey. He inherited the clockmaking business of his father-in-law but in 1711/12 moved to Nottingham, near the Pennsylvania-Maryland boundary line. In 1741 Benjamin Chandlee gave up clockmaking and moved from Nottingham to Wilmington, Delaware. Died in 1745.

Chaudron, Simon
w. m. & jeweler
Wholesale and retail dealer in "clocks, watches, jewellery and french china."
12 South Third St.   1798 (D)–1804 (D)

Chaudron, Simon & Co.
w. m. & jewelers
12 South Third St.   1805 (D)–1810 (D)
9 South Third St.   1811 (D)–1813 (D)
Simon Chaudron alone is listed at 5 South
Third St.   1814 (D)

Chaudron, Edward
w. m. & jeweler
9 South Third St.   1816 (D)

Chaudron & Rasch
Advertised as wholesale and retail dealers
in clocks and watches in 1812.

Child, Henry T.
w. m.
290 North Third St.   1841 (D)

Child, John
b. 1789, d. 1876
c. & w. m.
452 North Second St.   1813 (D)–1847 (D)

Chollot, John B.
c. & w. m.
253 North Second St.   1816 (D), 1817 (D)
148 North Fourth St.   1818 (D)–1820 (D)

Chrystler, William
w. m.
3 North Third St.   1828 (D)–1836 (D)

Clark, Benjamin
(also spelled Clarke)
c. & w. m.
advertised as early as 1791.
1 South Front St.   1793 (D)–1797 (D)
55 South Front St.   1798 (D)
61 High St.   1799 (D), 1800 (D)
Advertised removal to 36 Market (High)
June 4, 1800.
36 Market (High) St.   1801 (D)–1810 (D)
1 South Front St.   1811 (D)–1848 (D)
Benjamin Clark evidently retired in 1848,
but lived at least two years longer.

Clark, Ephraim
c. & w. m. Also sold and imported clocks.
Advertised as early as 1780.
Coomb's Alley bet. Second & Front Sts.
                              1785 (D)
1 South Front St.   1791 (D)
55 South Front St.   1793 (D)–1811 (D)
Nov. 19, 1791, Ephraim Clark advertised

as the successor to John Wood, Front and
Chestnut Sts. 55 South Front St. was corner of Chestnut St. Ephraim Clark evidently retired about 1812.

Clark, Ellis
c. & w. m.
1 South Front St.   1813 (D)–1825 (D)
                              1831 (D)–1839 (D)
32 Branch St.   1840 (D)
The address above was his home.
142 High St.   1841 (D)–1848 (D)

Clark, Ellis, Jr.
c. & w. m.
142 High St.   1842 (D)–1846 (D)
30 South Fourth St.   1847 (D)

Clark, Benjamin & Ellis
c. & w. ms.
1 South Front St.   1811 (D)–1840 (D)

Clark, Ephraim & Charles
c. & w. ms.
S.E. cor. Front & High Sts.
                              1806 (D)–1810 (D)
This address is same as 1 South Front St.

Clark, Charles
w. m.
42 North Fifth St.   1809 (D)

Clark, Edward
c. & w. m.
Fifth St. bet. South & Shippen   1797 (D)

Clark, Jesse
c. & w. m.
Corner Second & Lombard Sts.
                              1809 (D), 1810 (D)
227 South Second St.   1811 (D)–1814 (D)

Clark, Elias
c. & w. m.
43 High St.   1802 (D)

Clark, Thomas W.
w. m.
11 South Fourth St.   1839 (D)–1841 (D)

Clark & Hartley
w. ms.
11 South Fourth St.   1839 (D)–1841 (D)

Clarke, Benjamin W.
w. m.
11 North Sixth St.   1831 (D)

Clarke & Hutchinson
Cor. Almond & Front Sts.   1813 (D)

Clayton, Elias B.
w. m.
Beach above Maiden St.   1848 (D)
372 No. Second St.   1849 (D), 1850 (D)

Clein, John
w. m.
12 Myers Court   1831 (D)–1833 (D)

Conrad, Osborn
w. m.
319 Callowhill St.   1841 (D)
76 Sassafras St.   1842 (D)–1844 (D)
96 North Second St.   1845 (D)–1850 (D)

Cooper, Joseph B.
w. m.
4 South Sixth St.   1846 (D)

Cooper, Robert H.
w. m.
96 Germantown Road   1850 (D)

Corgee, Arthur
c. m.
412 South Front St.   1823 (D), 1824 (D)

Corvazier, Edward
w. m.
3 South 13th St.   1846 (D)

Cottey, Abel
c. m.
Born in England in 1655, died in Philadelphia 1711. The exact date of his coming to the Colonies is not known but he was established in Philadelphia as a clockmaker before 1700.
March 25, 1710, Benjamin Chandlee married Sarah, the daughter of Abel and Mary Cottey.

Coupar, Robert
In 1774 this man advertised skeleton watches for sale. Second St. opposite Friends' Meeting House.

Cox, Benjamin
w. m.
136 South Front St.   1809 (D), 1810 (D)
30 Powell St.   1811 (D)–1813 (D)

Cozens, Josiah B.
c. & w. m.
N.E. cor. Front & Arch Sts.
1818 (D)–1822 (D)
(73 North Front St.)
12 North Second St.   1823 (D), 1824 (D)

Cozens, J. B.
w. m. also clocks
S.W. cor. Harmony Court & Fourth St.
1823 (D), 1824 (D)
61 South Second St.   1825 (D)–1829 (D)

Crawley, John
c. & w. m.
15 Spruce St.   1803 (D)
134 South Front St.   1804 (D)
138 South Front St.   1805 (D)–1808 (D)
130 South Front St.   1809 (D)–1816 (D)
132 South Front St.   1817 (D)–1825 (D)

Crowley, E.
w. m.
132 South Fourth St.   1833 (D)

Crowley & Farr
c. & w. ms.
106 High St.   1823 (D), 1824 (D)
86 High St.   1825 (D)

Cure, Jule F.
w. m. & jeweler
149 South Sixth St.   1839 (D), 1840 (D)

Cure, Louis
w. m.
83 Mulberry St.   1813 (D)
193 North Third St.   1814 (D)
227 North Second St.   1816 (D), 1817 (D)
154 Sassafras St.   1818 (D)
154 Race St.   1819 (D), 1820 (D)

Curtis, Solomon
c. & w. m.
22 South Second St.   1793 (D)

D

Daft, Thomas
w. & c. m.
Advertised as early as March 1775, as being "late of London." Died 1793.

Dawson, Jonas
c. & w. m.
397 High St.   1813 (D)–1817 (D)

418 High St. 1818 (D)–1822 (D)
398 High St. 1823 (D), 1824 (D)

Deuconer, G.
c. m.
1 Myers Court 1817 (D)

Dominick, Frederick
Advertised between 1766 and 1777. In 1768 his shop was at S.W. cor. 2nd & Vine Sts. and he asked his countrymen (Germans) to patronize him.

Doull, James
c. & w. m.
Was at 8 Castle St. in 1825. In 1828 he moved to S.E. cor. Fourth & Spruce Sts. and remained there until 1840. He is not in the directories of 1841–1842.
In the directories of 1845 to 1849 James Doul (spelled with one "l") appears at the same address—Fourth & Spruce Sts. He was born in England and settled in Charlestown, Mass.

Douty, Henrick
Advertised as clockmaker in 1774.

Dowdney, Burrows
c. m.
Advertised 1768 to 1771. In 1768 his shop was in Front St., a few doors above Draw-bridge.

Droz, Charles
c. & w. m.
149 Walnut St. 1813 (D), 1814 (D)

Droz, Charles A.
c. & w. m.
118 Walnut St. 1816 (D)–1841 (D)

Droz, Hannah
w. m.
118 Walnut St. 1842 (D)–1850 (D)

Droz, Humbert (A. L.)
c. & w. m. also known as French watch-maker.
10 Mulberry (Arch) St.
1793 (D)–1799 (D)
28 Mulberry (Arch) St.
1801 (D)–1811 (D)

Droz & Sons
64 Chestnut St. 1807 (D)
149 Walnut St. 1808 (D)–1814 (D)

Drysdale, William
c. & w. m.
142 South Front St. 1816 (D)
144 South Front St. 1817 (D)–1821 (D)
44 High St. 1822 (D)–1824 (D)
3 South Fourth St. 1825 (D)–1831 (D)
93 South Fifth St. 1833 (D)
1 South Fifth St. 1835, 36 (D)
8 South Fifth St. 1837 (D)–1845 (D)
Walnut above Third St.
1846 (D)–1850 (D)

Drysdale, William Jr.
w. m.
8 South Fifth St. 1842 (D), 1843 (D)
20 South Sixth St. 1844 (D), 1845 (D)

Ducommun, A. L.
watchcase maker
62 Sassafras (Race) St. 1795 (D)–1798 (D)

Ducommun, H.
c. & w. m.
33 South Fourth St. 1843 (D)–1845 (D)
127 North Third St. 1846 (D)–1850 (D)

Ducommun, H. Jr. & Co.
w. m.
33 South Fourth St. 1843 (D), 1844 (D)

Duffield, Edward
Born Philadelphia County 1720, died in Lower Dublin (Philadelphia County) 1801. Worked at his trade of clock- and watchmaker in Philadelphia from 1741 to 1747 then moved to Lower Dublin. One of Duffield's clocks is in the rooms of the American Philosophical Society, of which he was a member. It was made in 1768.

Dupuy, Daniel
goldsmith, silversmith & watchmaker
4 South Second St. 1798 (D)–1804 (D)
114 Sassafras St. 1805 (D)–1808 (D)
Daniel Dupuy worked in Reading, Pa., for a short time about 1777. Died 1807.

Dupuy, Daniel, Jr.
goldsmith, silversmith & watchmaker
4 South Second St. 1799 (D)–1808 (D)
Died 1826.

Dupuy, John
c. & w. m.
Advertised 1769 to 1774.

In May 1774 his shop was in Second St., fourth door below Friends' Meeting House.
In 1803 he is listed in the directory as a watchmaker at 114 Sassafras St.

Dupuy, Odran
watchcase finisher
Advertised very early.

E

Elliott, Benjamin P.
w. m.
30 North Tenth St.   1843 (D)
198 Sassafras St.   1843 (D)–1846 (D)
3 South 13th St.   1847 (D)–1850 (D)

Elliott, James
jeweler
285 South Fifth St.   1804 (D)

Elson, Hermann
w. m.
107 North Second St.   1843 (D)
26 South Third St.   1844 (D), 1845 (D)
66 North Third St.   1846 (D)
207 Chestnut St.   1847 (D)
114 North 9th St.   1848 (D)

Elson, Julius
w. m.
15 South Fourth St.   1843 (D), 1844 (D)

Ent, Johann (John)
c. & w. m. & r.
Advertised in July 1763. Shop in Second St. bet. Arch & Race, "next door but one to Leonard Melchor's Tavern."

Evans, David
c. & w. m.
In Baltimore in 1773 David Evans advertised as clock- and watchmaker from Philadelphia.

Evans, William M.
c. & w. m.
309 High St.   1813 (D)–1818 (D)
287 High St.   1819 (D), 1820 (D)
301 High St.   1821 (D), 1822 (D)
South 13th St. S.W. cor. George St.
                                1825 (D)
50 South 13th St.   1831 (D)
Washington St. (West Phila.)
                                1839 (D)–1848 (D)

Eyre, Matthias
Made watch springs in Philadelphia.
Advertised in 1775.
Third St. below South St.

F

Faff, Augustus P.
c. m.
378 North Third St.   1837 (D)

Farr, John C.
c. & w. m.
23 Elfreth's Alley   1824 (D)
S.E. cor. Third & High Sts.
                                1825 (D)–1828 (D)
88 High St.   1829 (D)–1831 (D)
74 High St.   1833 (D)–1839 (D)
112 Chestnut St.   1840 (D)–1850 (D)

Farr, John C. & Co.
importers of watches & clocks
74 High St.   1837 (D)–1839 (D)
112 Chestnut St.   1840 (D)–1850 (D)

Favre, John James
c. & w. m.
14 Almond St.   1797 (D)

Ferris, Benjamin
w. m. also listed as c. m.
Born in Wilmington, Del., 1780. Came to Philadelphia upon reaching maturity.
17 North Second St.   1806 (D)
20 North Second St.   1807 (D)–1811 (D)

Ferris & M'Elwee
c. & w. ms.
20 North Second St.   1813 (D)

Fertig, Jacob W.
clock, watch & patent bellows maker
129 Sassafras St.   1810 (D)
82 North Front St.   1811 (D)

Fletcher, C. & G.
jewelers & clockmakers
N.E. cor. 3rd & Chestnut Sts.
                                1819 (D)–1822 (D)
130 Chestnut St.   1823 (D), 1824 (D)

Fletcher, Charles
w. m. & jeweler
N.E. cor. 3rd & Chestnut Sts.
        1817 (D), 1818 (D), 1824 (D), 1825 (D)
130 Chestnut St.   1829 (D)–1833 (D)

Fletcher, George
  jeweler
  122 Spruce St. 1821 (D)
  130 Chestnut St. 1825 (D)
  24 Little George St. 1829 (D)–1831 (D)

Fletcher, Leonard
  jeweler
  130 Chestnut St. 1819 (D)
  301 High St. 1820 (D)

Fletcher, Samuel
  jeweler
  339 North Second St. 1804 (D)

Fletcher, Thomas
  jeweler
  S.E. cor. Chestnut & Fourth Sts.
                    1813 (D)–1817 (D)
  130 Chestnut St. 1818 (D)–1836 (D)
  194 Chestnut St. 1837 (D)
  188 Chestnut St. 1839 (D)–1850 (D)

Fling, Daniel
  c. & w. m.
  97 North Second St. 1809 (D) 1811 (D)
  82 North Fourth St. 1813 (D), 1814 (D)
  324 North Second St. 1818 (D)
  John above Callowhill St.
                    1819 (D)–1822 (D)

Flower, Henry
  Advertised 1753-1755 as watchmaker.
  Second St. between Black Horse Alley &
  Chestnut.

Fries, John
  w. m.
  160 North Second St. 1844 (D)–1850 (D)

Fries, P.
  353 North Second St. 1844 (D)–1850 (D)

Fritz, C.
  clock repairer
  261 Green St. 1847 (D)
  147 Poplar St. 1848 (D)–1850 (D)

G

Gaensle, Jacob
  c. m.
  The son of John Gaensle, was born in
  Württemberg, Germany, in 1721 and came

to this country in 1743. He died in 1765.
This man was a clockmaker in Germantown.

Galbraith, Patrick
  c. & w. m.
  7 Dock St. 1794 (D)–1798 (D)
  271 South Second St. 1800 (D)
  286 South Front St. 1801 (D)
  30 Almond St. 1802 (D)–1810 (D)
  S.W. cor. Front & Almond Sts. 1811 (D)
  36 Cedar St. 1812 (D)–1817 (D)

Garrett, Philip
  c. & w. m. and machinist
  13 North Second St. 1801 (D), 1802 (D)
  138 High St. 1803 (D)–1808 (D)
  144 High St. 1809 (D)–1829 (D)
  11 South Fourth St. 1830 (D)–1833 (D)
  9 South Fourth St. 1835 (D)

Garrett, Philip & Sons
  c. & w. m.
  144 High St. 1828 (D), 1829 (D)
  11 South Fourth St. 1830 (D)–1833 (D)
  9 South Fourth St. 1835 (D)

Garrett, Thomas C.
  w. m.
  144 High St. 1829 (D), 1830 (D)
  11 South Fourth St. 1831 (D)–1833 (D)
  134 Market St. 1835 (D)
  11 South Fourth St. 1837 (D)
  21 Franklin Place 1839 (D), 1840 (D)

Garrett, Thomas C. & Co.
  jewelers
  76 High St. 1841 (D)
  11 South Fourth St. 1842 (D), 1843 (D)
  122 Chestnut St. 1844 (D)–1850 (D)

Garrett & Hartley
  w. ms.
  11 South Fourth St. 1837 (D)

Garrett & Haydock
  watchcase makers
  20 Franklin Place 1837 (D)
  21 Franklin Place 1839 (D), 1840 (D)

Gaw, William
  c. & w. m.
  7 Powell St. & 241 So. 2nd St. 1816 (D)
  84 North Front St. 1819 (D)–1822 (D)

Gensel, John

There is extant a one-hand wall clock with a brass dial which was made by John Gensel in Germantown. This clock appears very old but probably is not as old as its appearance might indicate. Little can be learned about John Gensel as a clockmaker, although the name Gensel was not uncommon in early Germantown. There is a clue to the identity of John Gensel in the record of Jacob Gaensle (Gensel), who was the son of John Gaensle and who was a clockmaker.

Godfrey, Thomas
w. m.

Born 1736, died 1763. This man was the son of Thomas Godfrey, Sr. The elder Godfrey—born in Bristol Township in 1704, died 1749—was the inventor of the mariner's quadrant, generally known as Hadley's quadrant. The son is often confused with the father. Thomas Godfrey, Sr., was apprenticed to a glazier and glazed the windows of Independence Hall when it was built. He had a natural genius for mathematics. Early in 1730 the elder Godfrey applied himself to the improvement of Davis's quadrant. In 1734 he wrote a letter to the Royal Society which was about to award the invention to its vice president, James Hadley, who had given notice of a similar quadrant. It would appear that the Royal Society sent Thomas Godfrey household furniture to the value of 200 pounds as a reward for his invention. Upon the death of the elder Thomas Godfrey in 1749, his son was apprenticed to a watchmaker. The younger Thomas Godfrey's talent for verse brought him to the attention of William Smith, provost of the University of Pennsylvania. Through Provost Smith he met a group of young men devoted to founding the arts of painting, music, and the drama in the Colonies. Among these were Benjamin West and Francis Hopkinson. Provost Smith secured the release of Thomas Godfrey as a watchmaker's apprentice and in 1758 also secured him a commission as ensign in the militia.

Goodfellow, William
c. & w. m.
24 Chestnut St.   1793 (D)
84 North Second St.   1794 (D)

40 Chestnut St.   1795 (D)–1797 (D)
114 Chestnut St.   1805 (D)
14 South Fourth St.   1808 (D)
64 Dock St.   1809 (D)–1811 (D)
173 High St.   1813 (D)
64 Dock St.   1818 (D)

Goodfellow, Wm. & Son
w. ms.
22 South Fourth St.   1799 (D)

Gordon, George
w. m.
238 North Second St.   1850 (D)

Green, John
w. & c. m.
104 Swanson St., Southwark   1794 (D)
Swanson St. near Perran's Alley   1796 (D)

Groff, J. R.
w. m.
58 High St.   1844 (D)–1850 (D)

Groppengiesser, J. L.
chronometer & clockmaker
69 South Front St.   1841 (D), 1842 (D)
100 South Third St.   1843 (D)–1850 (D)

Guile, John
w. m.
183 Cherry St.   1818 (D)–1824 (D)

H

Hahn, C. G.
w. m.
162 North Third St.   1798 (D)

Hall, John
w. m.
55 South Third St.   1804 (D)–1809 (D)
S.E. cor. Front & Chestnut Sts.
                    1811 (D)–1818 (D)
S.E. cor. Second & Union Sts.
                    1819 (D)–1824 (D)
88 Union St.   1825 (D), 1828 (D)
55 Dock St.   1829 (D)–1840 (D)

Hall, Peter
c. & w. m.
61½ South Second St.   1818 (D)–1824 (D)

Hansell, James
c. & w. m.
3 North Sixth St. 1816 (D)–1824 (D)
226 High St. 1825 (D)–1831 (D)
76 North Eleventh St. (residence)
1833 (D)
236 High St. 1835 (D)–1850 (D)

Harden, James
clock dial maker
18 Dock St. 1818 (D)–1824 (D)

Harpur, William E.
chronometer & watchmaker
136 Chestnut St. 1845 (D)–1850 (D)

Harrington, William
c. m.
Ridge Road above Green St.
1849 (D), 1850 (D)

Hartley, Jeremiah
w. m.
11 South Fourth St. 1837 (D)–1841 (D)
14 Franklin Place (residence) 1842 (D)
135 Cedar St. 1843 (D)–1850 (D)

Haydock, Eden
watchcase maker & jeweler
21 Franklin Place 1839 (D)–1841 (D)
11 South Fourth St. 1842 (D), 1843 (D)
122 Chestnut St. 1844 (D)–1850 (D)

The Heilig family of clockmakers
Hendrick Heilig, the founder of the family in Pennsylvania, was born in 1700, and in 1720 sailed from Amsterdam on the ship *Polly.* It is understood that he came from Hanover, Germany. He settled in Hanover Township, Montgomery County, and was a clockmaker and farmer. He married Susanna Rittenhouse and thus became the uncle of David Rittenhouse. He died in 1775 and together with his wife is buried in Methacton Mennonite Cemetery, Montgomery County.

John Heilig, Sr.
Born 1765, died 1841. Grandson of Hendrick Heilig, clockmaker and silversmith in Germantown. Was the first silversmith in Germantown. Church records show that he lived in Germantown in 1796.
167 North Front St. (in the city)
1801 (D), 1802 (D)
In 1800 John Heilig, Sr., occupied house now 6374 Germantown Road.

John Heilig, Jr.
c. & w. m.
Son of John Heilig, Sr. Had shop in Germantown 1824 to 1830. Died 1842.

Henry Daniel Heilig
Son of John Heilig, Jr., learned clockmaking in his grandfather's shop (John Heilig, Sr.). Died in 1830.

Jacob Heilig
Great-grandson of Hendrick Heilig. Born 1802. Clock- and watchmaker in Germantown in 1833.

John Heilig
watchmaker and brother of Jacob, was born in 1804.
Worked in Bridgeton, N. J. 1824 to 1839.
5 Ridge Road 1841 (D)–1847 (D)
Ninth & Ridge Road 1848 (D)–1850 (D)

Albert Elijah Heilig
Born 1834. Succeeded his father, Jacob Heilig, in business in Germantown.

Heineman, G.
w. m.
84 Mulberry St. 1849 (D)

Heineman, L. G.
w. m.
24 Walnut St. 1849 (D)
84 Mulberry St. 1850 (D)

Heiss, James P.
w. m.
43 North Eighth St. 1849 (D), 1850 (D)

Helm, Christian
w. m.
13 North Fifth St. 1802 (D), 1803 (D)
33 North Fifth St. 1804 (D)

Helm, Thomas
watchcase maker
147 Spring Garden St. 1839 (D),1840 (D)
10th near Parrish St. 1842 (D)
90 Cherry St. 1843 (D)
118 Chestnut St. 1844 (D), 1845 (D)
4 Hudson's Alley 1846 (D), 1847 (D)
143 Spring Garden St. (residence)
1848 (D)
Ranstead Place 1849 (D), 1850 (D)

Hepton, Frederick
w. m.
Vine St. bet. Second & Third Sts.   1785 (D)

Hight, Christian
w. m.
back of 257 Race St.   1819 (D)–1822 (D)

Hildeburn, Samuel
c. & w. m.
122 South Front St.   1810 (D)
132 South Front St.   1811 (D)–1814 (D)
72 High St.   1816 (D)–1844 (D)

Hildeburn, Woodworth
72 High St.   1816 (D)–1820 (D)

Hildeburn & Bros.
watches & jewelry
72 High St.   1850 (D)

Hildeburn & Watson
w. ms.
72 High St.   1833 (D)

Hodgson, William
c. & w. m.
Sixth St. bet. Arch & Market   1785 (D)

Hoffner, Henry
w. m.
148 North Front St.   1791 (D)

Holmes, J.
c. m.
646 North Second St.   1842 (D)

Hood, Jacob
jeweler
15 Quarry St.   1825 (D)

Hooper, B. C.
w. m.
60 Dillwyn St.   1848 (D)

Hopkins, H. P.
w. m.
136 High St.   1831 (D), 1832 (D)

Hopkins, Robert
w. & c. m.
Pine & 13th Sts.   1833 (D)

Hopper, Joseph M.
c. & w. m.
70 Green St.   1816 (D)
79 Green St.   1817 (D)
178 High St.   1819 (D)–1822 (D)

Howard, Thomas
c. & w. m.
Advertised 1787.
Second St. 7th door above Chestnut.
26 South Second St.   1791 (D)

Huckel, Jacob
w. m.
239 South Second St.   1824 (D)

Huckel, Samuel
c. & w. m.
Born 1798, died 1883.
38 Cedar St.   1818 (D)–1829 (D)
moved to Frankford.

Hugenin, Charles Frederick
c. & w. m.
83 Callowhill St.   1797 (D)–1798 (D)
11 North Fifth St.   1800 (D)–1802 (D)

Huston, William
c. & w. m.
Worked between 1767 and 1771. In the
will of John Wood, Jr., clockmaker, he
bequeathed a house in Front St., south of
Chestnut, which had been built by William Huston, but sold by the sheriff.

Hutchinson, Samuel
w. m.
158 High St.   1828 (D)
198 High St.   1829 (D)–1831 (D)
9 North Sixth St.   1833 (D)–1836 (D)
231 Market St.   1837 (D)–1839 (D)

Hutchinson, Thomas
c. & w. m.
73 North Front St.   1816 (D), 1817 (D)
120 South Front St.   1819 (D)–1824 (D)

J

Jacks, James
Advertised clocks and watches in Charleston, S.C., in 1787. In 1797 he was in Philadelphia and advertised his removal from
3rd & Market Sts. to 192 Market St. He
had for sale a great variety of goods besides clocks and watches—surveyor's and
navigator's instruments, billiard balls, and
harness furniture. It appears that he moved
back to Charleston in about 1800.

Jacks, William
jeweler
184 Market St.   1798 (D)–1800 (D)

Jeffreys, Samuel
c. & w. m.
Advertised 1771–1778. In 1771 he was located in Second St. between Christ's Church and the Court House. In 1777 he moved to Front St., corner Black Horse Alley, near the Coffee House.

Jerome, Chauncey
clocks
70 North Third St.   1846 (D)–1849 (D)

Job, John
c. & w. m.
271 North Front St.   1819 (D), 1820 (D)

Johnson, Robert
w. m.
Front St. opposite Drawbridge   1831 (D)
136 South Front St.
                    1833 (D), 1835–1836 (D)
Residence—20 Union St.   1837 (D)
132 South Front St.   1839 (D)–1850 (D)

Johnson, William E.
jeweler
Willow St. below Third St.   1841 (D)

Johnson & Crowley
c. & w. ms.
123 South Front St.   1832 (D)–1833 (D)

Johnson & Lewis
w. ms.
132 South Front St.   1837 (D)–1842 (D)

Jonas, Joseph
c. & w. m.
13 Spruce St.   1817 (D)

Joyce, Thomas
242 South Sixth St.   1821 (D), 1822 (D)
123 Plum St.   1823 (D)–1825 (D)

K

Karn, A. L.
c. & w. m.
159 South Front St.   1809 (D)

Kennedy, Hugh
w. m.
105 St. John St.   1845 (D)–1850 (D)

Kennedy, Patrick
c. & w. m.
23 Lombard St.   1795 (D)
61 South Second St.   1797 (D)
77 South Second St.   1799 (D)
87 South Second St.   1801 (D)

Kirchoff, J. H.
c. & w. m.
110 North Second St.   1805 (D)

Klein, John
w. m.
98 North Third St.   1828 (D), 1829 (D)
197 North Third St.   1831 (D)
2 Wood St.   1833 (D)
185 North Third St.   1835, 1836 (D)
Third above Wood St.   1837 (D)
197 North Third St.   1838 (D)–1850 (D)

Kline, Bartholomew
w. m., jeweler & silversmith
46 Charlotte St.   1842 (D)–1848 (D)
Randolph above Poplar St.   1850 (D)

Knowles, John
w. m.
1784, advertised that he moved to Second St. below Chestnut, 2nd door above Carter's Alley.

L

Lackey, Henry
c. m.
13 Elfreth's Alley   1808 (D)–1811 (D)

Ladomus, Jacob
w. m.
33 South Fourth St.   1843 (D)–1847 (D)
246 High St.   1848 (D)–1850 (D)

Ladomus, Lewis
w. m.
413½ High St.   1845 (D)–1850 (D)

Lamoine, A.
w. m.
176 North Fifth St.   1811 (D)–1814 (D)
311 South Second St.   1816 (D), 1817 (D)
This man's name was evidently also spelled "Lamvine" and "Lemvine."

Lane, James
c. & w. m.
79 North Front St.   1803 (D)
56 Cedar St.   1804 (D)
255 South Second St.   1805 (D), 1806 (D)
151 North Second St.   1807 (D)–1813 (D)
82 Sassafras St.   1816 (D)
165 North Front St.   1818 (D)

Laquain, Francis
c. & w. m.
4 North Second St.   1794 (D)

Latimer, James
w. m.
Born 1794, died 1826.
92½ Chestnut St.   1813 (D)–1822 (D)

Law, William
w. m. later musical instrument maker
13th St. above Shippen St.
                       1839 (D)–1841 (D)
149 South Sixth St.   1842 (D)
144 Cedar St.   1843 (D)–1846 (D)
13th St. above Cedar St.   1847 (D)
144 Cedar St.   1848 (D)–1850 (D)

Law, William P.
w. m.
150 Cedar St.   1849 (D), 1850 (D)

Leeds, Gideon H.
w. m.
2 North Sixth St.   1842 (D)

Lefferts, Charles
c. & w. m.
61½ South Second St.   1818 (D)–1822 (D)

Lefferts & Hall
c. & w. ms.
61½ South Second St.   1818 (D)–1822 (D)

Le Huray, Nicholas
w. & c. m.
South Second St. 4 doors below High
                       1809 (D), 1810 (D)
1 and 137 South Second St.   1811 (D)
263 North Second St.   1813 (D)
277 North Second St.   1814 (D)
170 North Second St.   1816 (D)
160 North Second St.   1817 (D)–1822 (D)
N.W. cor. Second & New Sts.
                       1823 (D)–1828 (D)

160 and 170 North Second St.   1829 (D)
160 North Second St.   1831 (D)
170 North Second St.   1833 (D)–1836 (D)
Note: There was a Nicholas Le Huray
who was a clockmaker in Delaware and
who had a shop at Ogletown on the road
from Christiana to Newark. His will was
probated in Delaware in 1834. It seems obvious that this was the same man who was
in business in Philadelphia. His son, Nicholas, Jr., evidently carried on the father's
name.

Le Huray, Nicholas, Jr.
w. & c. m.
160 North Second St.   1821 (D), 1822 (D)
170 North Second St.   1823 (D)–1840 (D)
172 North Second St.   1841 (D)–1846 (D)

Le Huray, Theodore
w. m.
172 North Second St.   1844 (D)
48 High St.   1846 (D)
72 North Second St.   1847 (D)–1850 (D)

Lemist, Wm., & Tappan, W. B.
clock & patent timepiece makers
3 South Third St.   1819 (D), 1820 (D)

Lescure, E. P.
watches & jewelry
76 North Second St.   1833 (D)–1836 (D)
S.E. cor. Third & High Sts.
                       1839 (D), 1840 (D)
5 South Fourth St.   1841 (D)
30 North Sixth St.   1842 (D), 1843 (D)
12 Noble St.   1844 (D)–1850 (D)

Leslie, Robert
A Scotsman, as a clock- and watchmaker
he pursued a very busy life. In 1789 he
was granted a patent for certain improvements in the mechanism of clocks. The first
patent was from the Assembly and then afterwards by the laws of Congress. Powerful combinations were formed in the trade
to oppose his innovations. He had many
other patents. In 1789 he proposed a museum but in 1793 advertised the return of
the subscriptions. In the directory of 1804
Robert Leslie is listed at 177 Mulberry
St. as "late watchmaker."
167 High St.   1791 (D)
79 High St.   1795 (D)
114 High St.   1803 (D)

Leslie, Robert, & Price, Isaac
c. & w. ms.
167 High St. 1793 (D)
79 High St. 1794 (D)–1800 (D)
March 13, 1799, the administrators of the
estate of Isaac Price advertised that they
wished to settle the affairs of Leslie &
Price.

Leslie & Parry
c. & w. ms.
245 High St. 1803 (D)
Note: It appears that in November 1795
Robert Leslie also was in partnership with
Abraham Patton under the firm name of
Robert Leslie & Co., 119 Market St., Balti-
more.

Levy, H. A.
w. m.
381 South Second St. 1846 (D)–1850 (D)

Levy, Lewis B.
w. m.
100 Cedar St. 1845 (D)

Levy, M. & Co.
c. ms.
194 High St. 1816 (D), 1817 (D)

Levy, Martin
watchcase maker
132 Vine St. 1814 (D), 1816 (D)
125 North Fifth St. 1817 (D)

Levy, Michael
c. & w. m.
151 Mulberry St. 1802 (D), 1803 (D)
23 North Fourth St. 1806 (D), 1807 (D)
192 North Fifth St. 1808 (D), 1809 (D)
14 Branner's Alley 1811 (D)
216 North Fifth St. 1813 (D), 1814 (D)
near 130 Vine St. 1816 (D)

Lewis, John
w. m.
144 South Front St. 1845 (D)–1850 (D)

Limeburner, John
w. m.
32 Cresson's Alley 1791 (D)

Lind, John
w. m.
39 Key's Alley 1791 (D)
50 Cable Lane 1801 (D)
Reported to have advertised as early as
1775.

Lindsay, Thomas
c. m.
Frankford.
"A contemporary of Seneca Lukens, father of Isaiah Lukens."

Linn, John
w. m.
37 Elm St. 1794 (D)
46 New Market St. 1799 (D)
39 Callowhill St. 1800 (D)
43 Callowhill St. 1805 (D)

Lohse & Kayser
Importers of watches
70 South Third St. 1831 (D)
79 High St. 1833 (D)–1836 (D)

Lovell & Smith
clocks
183 North Third St. 1841 (D)–1843 (D)

Lovell, A. E.
clocks
183 North Third St. 1844 (D)–1849 (D)

Low, Mark
w. m.
8 Jones' Court 1849 (D)
8 Sommers' Court 1850 (D)

Lownes, David
c. & w. m.
Third St. bet. Market & Chestnut 1785 (D)
33 South Third St. 1800 (D), 1802 (D),
1803 (D), 1804 (D), 1805 (D), 1807 (D)

Ludwig, John
w. m.
88 North Sixth St. 1791 (D)

Lukens, Isaiah
horologist, town clockmaker and mechanist.
Born 1779, died 1846. Son of Seneca Lukens, clockmaker of Horsham. Joined his
father in business upon coming of age.
Came to Philadelphia in about 1811. Prom-

inent in the establishment of The Franklin Institute. Member of the American Philosophical Society.
Back of 173 High St. 1818 (D)–1829 (D)
15 Decatur St. 1830, 1831 (D)
40 Carpenter St. 1837 (D)

M

Marks, Isaac
  dealer in watches
  36 Key's Alley 1795 (D)
  36 Coates Alley 1796 (D), 1797 (D)
  36 Cherry Alley 1798 (D)

Martin, John
  c. m.
  189 Germantown Road
                    1849 (D), 1850 (D)

Martin, Patrick
  c. & w. m.
  98 North Sixth St. 1821 (D), 1822 (D)
  N.W. cor. Sixth & Barclay's Court
                                1824 (D)
  257 Sassafras St. 1831 (D)–1833 (D)
  Meredith's Court 1837 (D)
  12 Noble St. (rear) 1839 (D)
  22 Harmony St. 1840 (D)–1843 (D)
  52 Passyunk Road 1845 (D)–1850 (D)

Mascher, John F.
  w. m.
  48 Brown St. 1850 (D)

Mathey, Lewis
  c. & w. m.
  158 North Second St. 1797 (D)–1800 (D)
  173 Market (High) St.
                    1801 (D)–1803 (D)

Matlack, William
  w. m.
  34 South Third St. 1797 (D)
  Advertised in Charleston, S.C., in 1787 that he had returned from Philadelphia. Advertised in Philadelphia in 1794.

Matlack, White
  c. m.
  Advertised Jan. 1777 at Market St. near Fourth, and as being "late of New York."

Matlack, White & William
  Advertised July 1780, South Side Market St. near Fourth.

Maus, Frederick
  c. & w. m.
  Second St. bet. Vine & Callowhill
                                1785 (D)
  194 North Second St. 1791 (D)–1793 (D)

Maxwell, A.
  c. & w. m.
  157 South Front St. 1805 (D)–1808 (D)
  163 South Front St. 1809 (D), 1810 (D)

Mayer, Elias
  wholesale jeweler & watches etc.
  48 South Third St. 1831 (D)–1833 (D)

Mecke, John
  c. & w. m.
  359 North Second St. 1849 (D), 1850 (D)

Mends, Benjamin
  c. & w. m.
  131 South Front St. 1796 (D), 1797 (D)

Mends, James
  c. & w. m.
  131 South Front St. 1795 (D)

Menzies, John
  Born in Scotland 1777, died in Philadelphia 1860.
  A well-known and prosperous watch- and clockmaker who was thoroughly established in Philadelphia in 1832 when he joined the St. Andrew's Society, an organization founded in 1749 to aid Scotsmen. His shop was at the corner of Front and Walnut Sts. He was something of a mechanical genius and built a "perpetual motion" machine which attracted wide attention until it ceased running. He was known as Captain Menzies and commanded a military organization known as the Caledonian Blues, the members of which were outfitted in Highland garb.

Merry, F.
  62 Race St. 1799 (D)

Miller, George
  c. & w. m.
  Germantown Ave. below Lafayette St. (now West Haynes St.) in Germantown in 1809.

Miller, George
  c. m.
  Morgan's Court 1829 (D)–1833 (D)

Miller, Thomas
w. m.
80 North Second St. 1819 (D), 1820 (D)
95 Mulberry St. 1823 (D), 1824 (D)
33 North Third St. 1829 (D)
97 Mulberry St. 1840 (D)

Miller, William
c. m.
12th St. below Callowhill St. 1847 (D)

Miller, William S.
c. m.
12th & Shippen Sts. 1843 (D), 1844 (D)
270 Cedar St. 1845 (D)–1848 (D)

Milne, Robert
c. & w. m.
69 Wood St. 1817 (D)

Moellinger, Henry
(Also spelled Mollinger.)
c. & w. m.
118 Sassafras St. 1794 (D)
1 North Third St. 1804 (D)

Monteith, Charles
c. m.
525 High St. 1847 (D)
517 High St. 1848 (D)

Murphy, Robert
w. m.
1 Montgomery St. 1848 (D), 1849 (D)

Mc

M'Coy, George W.
w. m.
213 Coates St. 1849 (D), 1850 (D)

M'Dowell, James
c. & w. m.
Died 1808
136 South Front St. 1794 (D)–1799 (D)
130 South Front St. 1801 (D)–1808 (D)
Residence, 82 South Fourth St. (D)–1798

M'Dowell, John
clocks, etc.
130 South Front St. 1817 (D)

M'Dowell, William Hanse
c. & w. m. also silversmith
Born 1795, died 1842.
130 South Front St. 1818 (D)–1836 (D)

M'Elwee, James
w. m.
20 North Second St. 1813 (D), 1814 (D)
Was in business with Benjamin Ferris.

McFarlane, Wm.
w. m.
5 Prune St. 1805 (D)

M'Ilhenney, Joseph E.
c. & w. m.
13 North Third St.
            1818 (D)–1823 (D), 1824 (D)
89 North Second St. 1825 (D)

M'Ilhenney & West
c. & w. ms.
13 North Third St. 1818 (D)–1822 (D)

M'Keen, Henry
w. m.
119 Chestnut St. 1823 (D), 1824 (D)
150 High St. 1825 (D)–1833 (D)
142 High St. 1837 (D)–1850 (D)

M'Mullen, Edward
c. m.
11 Callowhill St. 1846 (D)
Smith's Alley 1847 (D)
Bledisloe Place 1848 (D)

M'Pherson, Robert
w. m.
14 German St. 1850 (D)

N

Neisser, Augustine
Born in Sehlen, Moravia, 1717. In 1736 he
emigrated to Georgia and a few years later
came to Philadelphia and settled in Germantown. Married Catherine Reisinger in
1770 and had three sons. Died in 1780.
This man was an outstanding clockmaker.
In 1746 he was engaged to build the great
clock for the Moravian congregation in
Bethlehem, Pa. This was completed in
1747. Augustine Neisser was paid eight
pounds for his work.

Neisser, George B.
jeweler
315 North Front St. 1829 (D)
98 Green St. 1831 (D)–1833 (D)
465 North Third St. 1837 (D)–1839 (D)

Newberry, James (or J. W.)
c. & w. m.
367 North Third St. 1819 (D)–1822 (D)
33 South Front St. 1825 (D)
18 Frankford Road 1829 (D)–1850 (D)
In 1844 (D) this man added "dentist" to
watchmaking in his directory listing.

Newberry, J. & R.
w. ms.
near 125 South Second St. 1816 (D)

Nicollett, Joseph W.
w. m.
4 North Second St. 1798 (D)

Nicollett, Mary
w. m.
4 North Second St. 1799 (D)
Note: *Nicollett*, watchmaker, no first
name, is listed at 43 Walnut St. 1793 (D)

Nolen, Spencer
Clock dial manufacturer and painter. Later
became maker of looking glasses.
145 South Third St. 1816 (D)
12 Lombard St. 1817 (D)
8 South Third St. 1818 (D)–1824 (D)
83 South Second St. 1825 (D)
78 Chestnut St. 1828 (D)–1849 (D)
He seems to have gone into the looking-
glass business in 1825.

Nolen & Curtis
clock dial manufactory: clock & watch
tools & materials store
8 South Third St. 1818 (D), 1819 (D)
49 North Third St. 1820 (D), 1821 (D)
112 High St. 1822 (D) also listed at 49
North Third St. this year.

Norton, Thomas
c. & w. m.
Rising Sun and Germantown. Advertised
in 1794 as watchmaker, Rising Sun, Germantown Road.
Germantown Road, near Sign of the Rising Sun 1800 (D)–1811 (D)

O

Oertelt, Charles E.
w. m.
401 North Second St. 1844 (D)–1849 (D)
131 Cedar St. 1850 (D)

O'Hara, Charles
w. m.
134 South Front St. 1799 (D), 1800 (D)

Oliver, Griffith
c. m.
Arch St. between Second & Front
1785 (D)

Olwine, Henry
w. m.
Ridge Road above Eleventh St.
1849 (D), 1850 (D)

Ormsby, Henry
w. m.
366 North Second St. 1844 (D)–1850 (D)

Orr, Thomas
c. & w. m.
343 Sassafras St. 1809 (D), 1810 (D)
21 North Ninth St. 1811 (D)
17 Filbert St. 1813 (D), 1814 (D)
Maple St. 1816 (D)
back 90 Filbert St. 1817 (D)

Owen, Griffith
c. & w. m.
63 Mulberry St. 1791 (D)
73 Mulberry St. 1793 (D)–1811 (D)
In 1813 and 1814 directories the listing is
"enquire" 73 Arch (Mulberry) St.

Owen, John
c. m.
73 Mulberry St. 1818 (D)–1820 (D)

P

Palmer, John
French watchmaker
South Second St. & Spruce 1795 (D)
South Second St. bet. 171 & 177 1796 (D)

Parke, Augustus W.
c. & w. m.
126 Race St. 1819 (D), 1820 (D)
13 South Third St. 1822 (D)

Parke, Charles B.
w. m.
29 Callowhill St. 1807 (D), 1808 (D)
268 North Second St. 1809 (D), 1810 (D)

Parke, Solomon
c. & w. m.
179 North Front St. 1791 (D)
146 North Front St. 1794 (D)–1822 (D)

Parke, Solomon & Co.
c. & w. ms.
146 North Front St. 1797 (D)–1801 (D)

Parke, Solomon & Son
c. & w. ms.
146 North Front St. 1806 (D)–1808 (D)

Parker, Isaac
c. & w. m.
13 South Third St. 1819 (D)–1822 (D)
10 Shield's Court 1823 (D)–1825 (D)
20 Swanwick 1833 (D)
13 South Third St. 1835 (D)–1839 (D)
81 North Third St. 1840 (D)–1848 (D)
29½ North Fourth St. 1849 (D), 1850 (D)

Parker, Thomas
c. & w. m.
Born 1761, died 1833. Learned clockmaking under David Rittenhouse and John Wood. Began business in 1783. Had charge of State House clock. President of Mechanics Bank for 16 years, beginning 1814.
13 South Third St. 1793 (D)–1833 (D)

Parker, Thomas Jr.
c. & w. m.
51 Wood St. 1817 (D)
13 South Third St. 1818 (D)–1820 (D)
14 South Fourth St. 1821 (D), 1822 (D)

Parker & Co. (Thos. Parker & Co.)
c. & w. ms.
13 South Third St. 1818 (D)–1820 (D)

Parker, T. H.
manufacturer of clocks
6 Arcade E Ave. 1833 (D)

Parks, Augustus W.
c. & w. m.
126 Race St. 1819 (D), 1820 (D)
13 South Third St. 1833 (D)

Parmier, John Peter
w. m.
175 South Second St. 1793 (D)

Parrot, Frederick (or F. W.)
w. m.
Washington Ave., West Philadelphia
1847 (D)–1850 (D)

Parrot, Joseph
w. m.
469 Vine St. 1835 (D), 1836 (D)
Vine & 13th St. 1837 (D)–1842 (D)
Ann near Ridge Road 1843 (D)

Parry, John J.
Born 1773, died 1835. Nephew of Mrs. David Rittenhouse (Hannah Jacobs). Inherited Rittenhouse's tools upon death of the great clockmaker.
38 South Second St. 1794 (D)–1802 (D)
245 High St. 1803 (D), 1804 (D)
243 High St. 1805 (D)–1811 (D)
287 High St. 1813 (D), 1814 (D)
Cor. Chestnut & Sixth 1816 (D)–1822 (D)
252 High St. 1823 (D), 1824 (D)
319 High St. 1825 (D)–1829 (D)
2 North Sixth St. 1831 (D)–1835 (D)

Parsons, Henry R.
w. m.
144 North Second St. 1849 (D), 1850 (D)

Patton, Abraham
c. & w. m.
17 New St. 1799 (D)
87 New St. 1800 (D)
79 Market (High) St. 1801 (D)–1803 (D)
44 High St. 1804 (D)–1817 (D)
This man seems to have retired in 1818.

Patton & Jones
c. & w. ms.
44 High St. 1804 (D)–1814 (D)

Peale, James
c. m.
455 South Second St. 1814 (D)–1817 (D)

Pepper, Henry J.
w. m. & jeweler
103 Chestnut St. 1833 (D)–1836 (D)
66 Chestnut St. 1837 (D)–1844 (D)
167 Chestnut St. 1845 (D)–1850 (D)

Pepper, Henry J. & Son
w. ms. & jewelers
167 Chestnut St. 1846 (D)–1850 (D)

Perkins, Thomas
w. m. & cotton and wool card manufacturer.
120 South Front St. 1791 (D), 1793 (D),
1797 (D), 1799 (D)
In May 1793 Thomas Perkins advertised that he would discontinue business June 1 next. He then became a "patent nail manufacturer." But in 1799 he was again a watchmaker.

Perpignann, Peter
w. m. & jeweler
359 North Third St. 1821 (D)–1824 (D)
Quarry St. near Third 1825 (D)

Peters, James
clock and thimble manufacturer, also gold- and silversmith.
65 Arch (Mulberry) St.
1821 (D)–1825 (D)
89 North Second St. 1828 (D)–1831 (D)
105 North Second St. 1835 (D)–1850 (D)
In 1837 this versatile man also became a spectacles manufacturer but continued to make thimbles.

Petty, Henry
c. m.
378 North Third St. 1829 (D)–1833 (D)

Pfaff, August (also Augustin)
German clockmaker
378 North Third St. 1831 (D)–1836 (D)
505 North Third St. 1839 (D)–1850 (D)

Pfaff, Henry
c. m.
378 North Third St. 1829 (D)–1833 (D)

Pfluefer, Hermann
w. m.
46 North Fourth St. 1849 (D), 1850 (D)

Pickering, Joseph
c. & w. m.
315 North Front St. 1816 (D)–1833 (D)
Front & Master Sts. 1837 (D)–1849 (D)
In 1839 Pickering lists himself as "screw manufacturer."

Pierret, Matthew
French watchmaker
143 North Front St. 1795 (D), 1796 (D)

Platt, John
c. m.
George above Apple St. 1843 (D)

Ponson, Peter
w. m.
Moravian Alley 1796 (D)

Praefelt, John
c. & w. m.
Fifth St. bet. Lombard & Pine Sts.
1797 (D), 1798 (D)

Price, Benjamin
c. & w. m. and copperplate printer
71 Lombard St. 1828 (D)

Price, Isaac
c. & w. m.
Died Oct. 1798.
86 High St. 1791 (D)
79 High St. 1793 (D)–1797 (D)

Price, Philip
w. m.
68 Union St. 1824 (D)

Price, Philip, Jr.
c. & w. m.
31 South Fourth St. 1813 (D), 1814 (D)
147 Chestnut St. 1816 (D), 1817 (D)
71 High St. 1818 (D)–1825 (D)
66 Lombard St. 1828 (D)–1844 (D)
In 1825 Philip Price, Jr., added copperplate printing to clockmaking and gradually came to devote his whole time to that business.

Probasco, Jacob
c. & w. m.
369 North Second St. 1822 (D)

Purse, John
c. & w. m.
458 North Third St. 1803 (D)

R

Read, Daniel I.
w. & c. m.
271 South Front St. 1798 (D)

Read, William H. J.
w. & c. m.
46 Chestnut St.   1831 (D)–1836 (D)
44 Chestnut St.   1837 (D)–1850 (D)

Reed, Frederick
c. & w. m.
150 Market St.   1818 (D)–1822 (D)

Reed, G. Washington
w. m.
N. W. cor. Second & Vine Sts.
            1843 (D)–1850 (D)

Reed, Isaac
c. & w. m.
N. W. cor. Second & Vine Sts.
            1819 (D)–1822 (D)
176 North Second St.   1823 (D)–1846 (D)

Reed, Isaac & Son
c. & w. m.
176 North Second St.   1837 (D)–1850 (D)

Reed, John W.
c. m.
Travis' Court   1846 (D), 1847 (D)

Reed, Osman
w. m.
176 North Second St.   1831 (D)–1841 (D)
74 High St.   1842 (D)–1850 (D)

Reed, Osman & Co.
w. ms.
74 High St.   1841 (D)–1843 (D)

Reeve, George
w. m.
next to 55 North Water St.   1804 (D)
120 High St.   1805 (D)

Reeve, Richard
c. & w. m.
Corner Mulberry & Water Sts.
            1803 (D)–1807 (D)

Reeve, Richard & George
w. ms.
120 High St.   1804 (D)

Reeves, David S.
c. & w. m.
94 North Fourth St.   1831 (D)–1836 (D)

Reiley, John
(also spelled Riley)
Second St. bet. Market & Chestnut
            1785 (D)
11 South Second St.   1791 (D)–1814 (D)
In 1805 John Reiley listed himself as "bottler and watchmaker" and in 1813 he gave up watchmaking to list himself as the proprietor of a "wine and liquor store."

The Richardson family
Francis Richardson, a silver- and goldsmith, founded a family famous in these crafts. He engraved clock dials and probably purchased the works from other Philadelphia clockmakers. However, the following advertisement appeared in the Pennsylvania Gazette for Sept. 4–16, 1736: "Very neat clocks and jacks made, sold, cleaned and mended reasonably by Francis Richardson, Goldsmith, Corner of Letitia Court in Market St." He was born in New York in 1681 and brought to Philadelphia at the age of nine. In 1717 he was admitted as a freeman. It appears that he was working as a silversmith in Philadelphia shortly after 1700.

Joseph Richardson (born 1706, died 1770, according to newspaper notice of his death) was the son of Francis and was associated with his father in business.

Joseph Richardson, Jr. (born 1752, died 1831), and *Nathaniel Richardson* (born 1754, died 1827) were sons of Joseph.

Riehl, George
w. m.
199 Mulberry St.   1805 (D)

The Riggs family of clockmakers
William H. C. Riggs founded a firm which became very active in furnishing clocks for railroads and also in servicing chronometers for captains of vessels using the Port of Philadelphia. The history of the firm as traced from directories is as follows:

Riggs, Wm. H. C.
c. & w. m.
89 Chestnut St., corner of Third
            1819 (D)–1821 (D)
29 South Fourth St.   1822 (D)
112 High St.   1825 (D)
34 Chestnut St.   1828 (D), 1829 (D)

67 South Front St. 1831 (D)–1834 (D)
watch and chronometer maker
126 South Front St. 1840 (D)–1842 (D)
126 South Front St. and 13 Dock St.
1843 (D)–1860 (D)
244 South Front St. 1861 (D)

Riggs W. H. C. & Son (Daniel)
244 South Front St. 1863 (D)

Riggs Daniel & Co.
244 South Front St. 1864 (D), 1865 (D)

Riggs & Brother
(Daniel & Robert Riggs)
244 South Front St. 1866 (D)–1870 (D)

Riggs and Brother
nautical instrument makers
244 South Front St. 1871 (D)

Riggs Brothers
watches
244 South Front St. and 116 South
Fourth St. 1872 (D)–1877 (D)
221 Walnut St. 1879 (D)
This firm has continued in business until
the present day. The history is only given
up to 1879, since that covers the period interesting to collectors.

Riley, Robert
w. m.
30 Moravian Alley 1806 (D), 1807 (D)

Ritchie, George
c. & w. m.
Cor. Second & Market Sts. 1785 (D)
171 North Third St. 1807 (D)
213 North Second St. 1810 (D)
back 3 Watkin's Alley 1811 (D)

Rittenhouse, Benjamin
Brother of David Rittenhouse, Benjamin
was born at Norriton, Pa., in 1740. He was
reared and educated at Norriton, joined
the army in the Revolution and was
wounded at the Brandywine. Was superin-
tendent of government gun lock factory in
Philadelphia in 1778. Judge of the Common
Pleas Court in Montgomery County in
1791. He was both a clock and instrument
maker.
Listed in Directory of 1807 as surveying
instrument maker, no address.
Mathematical instrument maker
Pine above 12th St. 1819 (D)
258 Arch St. 1820 (D)

Rittenhouse, David
Born 1732, died 1796. Philadelphia and
Norriton, Montgomery Co. The pioneer
American astronomer was born in what is
now a part of Philadelphia and at the age
of two was taken to Norriton, near Norristown. By 1749 he had established himself
as a clockmaker and surveyor. In 1763 he
surveyed the boundary between Delaware
and Pennsylvania with instruments of his
own making. He observed the transit of
Venus with instruments of his own making
in 1769. In 1770 he moved to Philadelphia
to the southwest corner of Seventh and
Arch Sts., and on the opposite corner
he built an astronomical observatory
which, for many years, was the only observatory in the United States. He pursued
a very busy life in scientific endeavors and
in public service. In 1791 he succeeded
Benjamin Franklin as president of the
American Philosophical Society. Rittenhouse built two orreries, one for Princeton
University and one for the University of
Pennsylvania. He died in Philadelphia on
June 26, 1796.

Robbins, George
w. m.
345 High St. 1849 (D), 1850 (D)

Roberts, F.
manufacturer of patent mantel clocks
46 North Fifth St. 1828 (D), 1829 (D)

Roberts, John
c. & w. m.
47 South Third St. 1797 (D)–1799 (D)

Roberts, William
c. & w. m.
73 North Third St. 1821 (D)

Robeson, Isaac
w. m.
Washington above 6th St. 1846 (D)

Rode, William
w. m.
10 High St. 1795 (D)

Rohr, John A.
w. m. & jeweler
113 North Second St. 1807 (D)
116 North Second St. 1808 (D)–1813 (D)

Rudolph, Samuel
c. & w. m.
157 South Front St. 1803 (D)

Rue, Henry
w. m.
116 Dilwyn St. 1835, 1836 (D)

Russell, George
w. m.
18 North Sixth St. 1833 (D)–1850 (D)

S

Sampson, William
c. & w. m.
316 North Front St. 1802 (D), 1803 (D)

Sandoz, Charles H.
w. m.
187 North Second St. 1800 (D)
Cauffman's Court 1801 (D), 1802 (D)

Sandoz, Louis
w. m.
12 Tammany St. 1845 (D)

Sauer, Christopher
(Also spelled "Saur," "Souer" and "Sower.")
Born in Wittgenstein, Westphalia, in west-
central Germany in 1693. Arrived in Pennsylvania in 1724 and went to Germantown.
Built home in Germantown in 1731. In
1738 he set up his printing press. Died 1758.
Christopher Sauer was a very versatile
man. When he arrived in Germantown he
considered many lines of endeavor for a
livelihood: clockmaking—"because it was
tedious and expensive to bring in clocks
from the old country"—oculist, cabinet
work, book making and medicine. He had
studied medicine at Marburg. In seeking
herbs for his medical work he went into
the Conestoga country and for a while settled in what is now Leacock township,
Lancaster County. Here his wife came
under the influence of Conrad Beisel and
entered the "convent" at Ephrata. Sauer
returned to Germantown with his son. He
spent much time with Dr. Christopher
Witt and for a while divided his time with
the occupations of clock- and watchmaker,
apothecary and oculist. He finally turned
to printing and set up a press to defend the
interests of German immigrants. From this
press he issued the first newspaper in the
Colonies printed in German type and the
first Bible issued in the New World.

Saxton, Joseph
c. & w. m.
94 Chestnut St. 1823 (D), 1824 (D)
Born 1799, Huntingdon, Pa., died 1873.
Went into his father's nail factory, then
was apprenticed to watchmaker. At age of
18 went to Philadelphia, where he set up as
a watchmaker, but left this work to take
up engraving. Then associated himself
with Isaiah Lukens. Later went to England,
where he associated himself with Adelaide
Gallery of Practical Science. Recalled from
England in 1837 to become balance maker
at the U. S. Mint in Philadelphia. In 1843
went to Washington with Coast Survey.
Was ill 15 years before his death. In October 1824 Joseph Saxton exhibited a new
clock with a new escapement at The
Franklin Institute Exhibition. The friction
of this ingenious clock was so diminished
that it required no oil for the pallets.

Schell, Samuel F.
w. m.
192 North Third St. 1833 (D)
Lawrence above Wallace
1835 (D), 1836 (D)

Scherr, Lewis
clocks
49 Brown St. 1846 (D)–1850 (D)

Schreiner, Charles W.
c. & w. m.
73 North Third St. 1813 (D), 1814 (D)
78 North Third St. 1816 (D)–1831 (D)
52 North 11th St.
1833 (D)–1835, 1836 (D)
59 North 11th St. 1837 (D)–1839 (D)

Schuller, J.
c. m.
89 St. John St. 1845 (D)
Marshall & Willow Sts. 1846 (D)

Schulz, Gottlieb
c. & w. m.
475 North Second St. 1821 (D), 1822 (D)

Schume, Thomas
c. & w. m.
69 Chestnut St. 1825 (D)

Seddinger, Margaret
w. m.
Linn near Nixon St.   1846 (D)

Servoss, Charles
c. m.
Parrish above 11th St.   1849 (D)

Servoss, Joseph S.
clocks, looking glasses & fancy hardware
60 North Second St.   1845 (D)–1847 (D)
204 North Second St.   1848 (D)
206½ North Second St.
                    1849 (D), 1850 (D)

Shearman, Robert
(Also spelled Sheerman and Sherman.)
c. & w. m.
339 North Second St.   1799 (D)
337 North Third St.   1800 (D), 1801 (D)
333 North Third St.   1803 (D), 1804 (D)
Robert Shearman was in business in Wilmington, Delaware, in 1768.

Shermer, John
c. & w. m.
132 North Fourth St.   1803 (D)
81 North Fifth St.   1804 (D)
32 Crown St.   1805 (D), 1806 (D)
384 North Second St.   1807 (D)–1813 (D)

Shippen, William A.
w. m.
52 Cedar St.   1821 (D)
5 Summer's Court   1822 (D)
241 South Second St.   also 1822 (D)
N. E. cor. Front & Mulberry Sts.
                    1823 (D), 1824 (D)

Shuler, John
c. m.
96 St. John St.   1848 (D), 1849 (D)

Simpson, Alexander J.
watchcase maker
21 Franklin Place   1848 (D)

Simpson & Brother
watchcase makers
21 Franklin Place   1849 (D), 1850 (D)

Sines, Hiram L.
Clocks & Shoes
164 North Second St.   1848 (D), 1849 (D)

Sleeper & Jeannert
watches & jewelry
30 South Sixth St.   1850 (D)

Smart, John
w. m.
306 High St.   1847 (D)–1850 (D)

Smick, Peter
watchcase maker
Monroe near Palmer (Kensington)
                    1848 (D)

Smith, Frederick
w. m. & watchcase maker
97 Chestnut St.   1843 (D)–1846 (D)
118 Chestnut St.   1847 (D)
52½ Chestnut St.   1849 (D), 1850 (D)

Smith, F. C.
clocks
104 North Third St.   1844 (D)

Smith, Hezekiah
w. m.
Apple above George St.   1845 (D)

Smith, Isschar
w. m.
Apple near George St.
                    1842 (D), 1843 (D)
In 1847 this man is listed as a blacksmith.

Smith, James
c. m.
104 North Third St.   1839 (D)–1841 (D)
82 North Third St.   1842 (D)–1850 (D)

Smith, Philip
watchcase maker
5 Drinker's Alley   1847 (D), 1848 (D)
8 Harmony Court   1849 (D), 1850 (D)

Smith, Robert
c. & w. m.
331 North Second St.   1821 (D)
302 North Second St.   1822 (D)
101 South Fifth St.   1825 (D)
20 Little George St.   1828 (D)
12 Little George St.   1829 (D)
21 Wood St.   1831 (D)

Smith & Goodrich
clocks & looking glasses
183 North Third St.   1850 (D)

Smitten, R. T.
w. m.
Thompson above Thirteenth St.
1846 (D), 1847 (D)

Solliday, Daniel H.
w. & c. m.
Daniel Hinckel Solliday—born in Sumneytown, Montgomery County, son of John
Sallade, clockmaker. Worked as clockmaker in Sumneytown until 1823. From
1824 to 1828 active in Evansburg, Lower
Providence Township.
193 North Third St. 1829 (D)
186 Callowhill St. 1831 (D)–1850 (D)

Somerdike, William
watchcase maker
George above 13th St. 1849 (D)
Juniper & George Sts. 1850 (D)

Somers & Crowley
c. & w. m.
132 South Fourth St. 1828 (D)–1833 (D)

Souza, Samuel
w. m.
N. E. cor. Walnut & Fourth Sts.
1819 (D), 1820 (D)

Sperry, William
c. m. & clock dealer
20 Garden St. 1843 (D)
254 Wood St. 1844 (D)–1847 (D)
Cedar above Broad St. 1849 (D)

Sprogell, John
448 North Second St. 1791 (D)

Spurch, Peter
c. & w. m.
Third, between Green & Coate's Sts.
1794 (D)
9 Strawberry St. 1795 (D)
7 North Front St. 1796 (D)
86 North Fourth St. 1798 (D)–1806 (D)

Statzell, P. M.
w. m.
172 North Second St. 1847 (D)–1850 (D)

Steine, Abraham
dealer in watches
86 North Third St. 1795 (D)–1824 (D)
84 North Third St. 1825 (D)–1828 (D)

44 South Front St. 1791 (D)–1793 (D)

Stellwagen, Charles K.
w. m.
220 Chestnut St. 1848 (D)

Stillas, John
c. & w. m.
Front between Market & Chestnut Sts.
1785 (D)

Stollenwerck, P. M.
c. m. & "mechanist in general"
Eleventh above High St.
1813 (D), 1814 (D)

Stout, Samuel
w. m.
492½ North Second St. 1847 (D)

The Stretch family of clockmakers
Peter Stretch
Born 1670, died 1746. Came to Pennsylvania from Leek, Staffordshire, England,
in 1702. His uncle was a famous clockmaker in England. Peter Stretch used ar-
rows on hands of his clocks.

Thomas Stretch
Son of Peter Stretch. Died 1765. Thomas
Stretch used fleur-de-lys on hands of his
clocks. One of the founders, and first governor, of The State in Schuylkill, famous
old fishing club. Made State House Clock
in 1753.

William Stretch
Another son of Peter Stretch.

Samuel S. Stretch
Nephew of Peter Stretch.
Clockmaker. Died 1732.

Isaac Stretch
Clockmaker. Grandson of Peter Stretch.
Advertised in 1752.

Stuart, James
w. m.
231 High St. 1847 (D)–1850 (D)

Syderman, Philip
w. & c. m.
South Alley bet. Fifth & Sixth Sts.
1785 (D)

Syng, Philip
w. m. and silversmith
Born Cork, Ireland, 1703, died 1789. Came
to Philadelphia with his family at 17 and
took up his trade of watchmaking. He became associated with Franklin in many enterprises and was one of the founders of
the University of Pennsylvania. He was
also, for a time, treasurer of the County of
Philadelphia. Syng made the writing para-
phernalia used in signing the Declaration
of Independence. Despite his prominence
he continued to sell watches until the time
of his death.

T

Taf, John James
w. m.
128 Sassafras St. 1794 (D)

Tappan, William B.
c. m.
49 North Third St. 1818 (D)
3 South Third St. 1819 (D), 1820 (D)

Taylor, Luther
c. & w. m.
51 North Third St. 1823 (D)–1825 (D)
132 Locust St. 1828 (D)
127 Lombard St. 1829 (D)
7th St. near Green 1831 (D)–1833 (D)
263 North Seventh St. 1836 (D)

Taylor, Samuel
c. & w. m.
Cor. Water & High Sts.
1798 (D), 1799 (D)

Tazewell, Samuel O.
This clockmaker is mentioned in a deed of
1812. He made tall case clocks in the
Sheraton style, some of which have survived.

The Thibault family of jewelers, watchmakers, dealers in clocks, and gold- and silversmiths
Thibault, Francis, the elder
goldsmith & jeweler
87 South Front St. 1800 (D), 1801 (D)
209 Cedar St. 1802 (D)
This man died in 1802.

Thibault & Co.
goldsmiths & jewelers
251 South Second St. 1797 (D), 1798 (D)
Francis Thibault, the elder, was the Thibault of this firm.

Thibault, Francis & Felix
jewelers
172 South Second St. 1807 (D)–1809 (D)
This Francis Thibault is Francis the
younger.

Thibault & Brothers
jewelers
66 South Second St. 1810 (D)–1824 (D)
150 Chestnut St. (S.E. cor. Fifth)
1825 (D)–1836 (D)

Thibault, Francis, Frederick & Felix
jewelers
66 South Second St. 1813 (D), 1814 (D)

Thibault, Felix
jeweler
66 South Second St. 1814 (D)
49 Almond St. 1816 (D), 1817 (D)
66 South Second St. 1818 (D)–1824 (D)
150 Chestnut St. 1825 (D)–1836 (D)
Spruce near Front 1837 (D)
Felix Thibault retired in 1837.

Thibault, Francis, the younger
jeweler
15 Franklin Court 1816 (D)
24 Powell St. 1817 (D)
66 South Second St. 1818 (D)–1822 (D)
150 Chestnut St. 1825 (D)–1831 (D)

Thibault, Frederick
goldsmith, silversmith, and jeweler
66 South Second St. 1818 (D)–1824 (D)
150 Chestnut St. 1825 (D)–1836 (D)

Thornton, Andrew
w. m.
130 South Front St. 1811 (D)

Thornton, Joseph
c. & w. m.
26 South Third St. 1819 (D), 1820 (D)

Thum, Charles
w. m.
4 North Sixth St. 1828 (D), 1829 (D)
376 North Second St. 1831 (D)
60 Tammany St. 1833 (D)

Townsend, Charles
c. & w. m.
136 South Front St. 1799 (D)–1804 (D)
In 1805 (D) Charles Townsend is listed at
both above address and 105 Chestnut St.
This double listing continues to 1808 (D).
105 Chestnut St. 1809 (D)–1825 (D)
S.E. cor. 10th & Chestnut Sts.
                            1828 (D)–1833 (D)
21 Walnut St. 1835 (D)
Tenth near Chestnut (21 South 10th)
                            1837 (D)–1842 (D)
49 South Tenth St. 1843 (D)–1849 (D)
In 1850 (D) Charles Townsend had evidently given up his shop and is at his
dwelling house 138 South Tenth St.

Townsend, Charles, Jr.
c. & w. m.
Sixth St. below High (24 South Sixth)
                            1829 (D)–1836 (D)
167 Chestnut St. 1837 (D)–1843 (D)
66 Chestnut St. 1844 (D)
29 Dean St. 1845 (D)–1850 (D)

Townsend, Elisha
w. m.
Chestnut St. above Thirteenth 1829 (D)

Townsend, John, Jr.
c. & w. m.
169 South Second St. 1811 (D)
180 South Second St. 1813 (D)–1816 (D)
2 North Fifth St. 1818 (D)–1820 (D)
1 North Fifth St. 1821 (D), 1822 (D)
2 North Fifth St. 1823 (D)–1825 (D)
90 South Second St. 1828 (D)
346 High St. 1829 (D)
14 North Fifth St. 1831 (D)–1833 (D)

Townsend, John
w. m.
Washington St. (West Philadelphia)
                            1849 (D)

Tracy, Charles
watchcase maker
112 Chestnut St. 1843 (D), 1844 (D)
106 Chestnut St. 1845 (D)–1850 (D)

Tracy, C. & E.
watchcase makers
106 Chestnut St. 1846 (D)–1850 (D)

Tracy, William
w. m.
1 Adams St. 1844 (D)–1850 (D)

Trahn, Peter C.
c. m.
Hanover St. near Frankford Road
                            1845 (D)–1849 (D)

Treadwell, Oren B.
c. & w. m.
82 North Seventh St. 1846 (D)–1849 (D)
This man is first listed as "painter."

V

Vaughan, David
A watchmaker mentioned by Penn as being
in Philadelphia in 1695.

Voight, Henry
clockmaker and chief coiner of U.S. Mint
Born 1738, died 1814.
Second St. bet. Vine and Race 1785 (D)
149 North Second St.
                            1791 (D)–1793 (D)
In 1780 Henry Voight had a wire mill in
Reading, Pa. He went to Philadelphia
shortly after this date. His acquaintance
with John Fitch, inventor of the steamboat,
dated from 1786. In 1787, he became a
shareholder in Fitch's company and held
five shares. In 1792 he entered into formal
partnership with Fitch for the manufacture
of steam engines but after a quarrel this
project fell through. In 1793 he invented
a method for making steel from bar iron
and about the same time became chief
coiner at the Philadelphia Mint, a position
he held until his death.

Voight, Thomas
(Also Thomas H.)
c. m.
44 North Seventh St. 1811 (D)–1836 (D)
Son of Henry Voight. Thomas Voight
made the Jefferson clock now in the possession of the Historical Society of Pennsylvania. In 1826 Jefferson's daughter,
Martha Randolph, presented the clock to
Dr. Robley Dunglison—tradition says in
settlement of accounts for medical services.
In 1894 William Ladam Dunglison presented the clock to the Historical Society.

Voight, Sebastian
c. m.
Evidently a brother of Henry Voight.
149 North Second St.   1794 (D)–1798 (D)
173 Market St.   1799 (D), 1800 (D)

W

Waage & Norton
w. ms.
31 South Third St.   1798 (D)

Waples, Nathaniel
c. & w. m.
58 High St.   1816 (D)–1820 (D)

Ward & Govett (Anthony Ward)
w. ms.
N.W. cor. Front & High Sts.   1813 (D)
23 North Second St.   1814 (D)

Ward, Jehu
c. & w. m. & silversmith
7th St. near Pine   1808 (D)
134 South Front   1810 (D)
145 Chestnut St.   1811 (D)–1814 (D)
44 High St.   1819 (D), 1820 (D)
42 High St.   1821 (D)–1837 (D)
92 High St.   1839 (D)–1844 (D)
106 Chestnut St.   1846 (D)–1848 (D)
In 1819 Jehu Ward took over the stand of
Abraham Patton, 44 High St.

Ward, Isaac
c. & w. m.
315 North Front St.   1811 (D)
Front & High Sts.   1813 (D)
315 North Front St.   1814 (D)
Newmarket above Pegg's Run   1818 (D)

Ward, William L.
w. m. & jeweler
42 High St.   1831 (D)–1837 (D)
92 High St.   1839 (D)–1843 (D)
106 Chestnut St.   1845 (D)–1850 (D)

Ward & Cox
c. ms. & silversmiths
145 Chestnut St.   1811 (D)

Ward, J. & W. L. (Jehu & William L.)
watches & jewelry
42 High St.   1837 (D)
106 Chestnut St.   1845 (D)

Ward, J. & Co. (Jehu)
w. ms.
92 High St.   1843 (D)

Ward, J. & W. L. & Co.
w. ms.
92 High St.   1839 (D)–1842 (D)

Ward, Edward H.
w. m.
92 High St.   1840 (D)–1842 (D)
In 1843 Edward H. Ward became an M.D.

Wark, William
w. m.
428½ High St.   1848 (D)–1850 (D)

Warner, Cuthbert
w. m. & watchcase maker
Washington below 11th St.   1840 (D)
90 Cherry St.   1841 (D)–1843 (D)
118 Chestnut St.   1844 (D)–1846 (D)
4 Hudson's Alley   1847 (D), 1848 (D)
Ranstead Place   1849 (D), 1850 (D)

Warner, John S.
gold & silver watchcase manufacturer
Greenleaf Court   1833 (D)–1839 (D)
26 Merchant St.   1844 (D), 1845 (D)
Greenleaf Court ran from Fourth St. between Market & Chestnut Sts. It was evidently later named Merchant St.

Warner, Joseph P.
watchcase maker
5 Dilk's Court   1837 (D)
near 7 Cherry St.   1839 (D)

Warner, Robert P.
watchcase & gold dial maker
54 Lawrence St.   1839 (D), 1840 (D)
90 Cherry St.   1842 (D), 1843 (D)
118 Chestnut St.   1844 (D)–1846 (D)
4 Hudson's Alley   1847 (D), 1848 (D)
Ranstead Place   1849 (D), 1850 (D)

Warner, William
watchcase maker
90 Cherry St.   1839 (D)–1842 (D)
Green below 12th St.   1848 (D)
Ranstead Place   1849 (D), 1850 (D)

Warner & Keating
watchcase makers
26 Greenleaf Court (Merchant St.)
                          1840 (D)–1843 (D)

Warner & Newlin
gold dial makers
4 Hudson's Alley 1848 (D)
Ranstead Place 1849 (D), 1850 (D)

Warner, William & Co.
watchcase makers
118 Chestnut St. 1844 (D)–1846 (D)
4 Hudson's Alley 1847 (D), 1848 (D)
Ranstead Place 1849 (D), 1850 (D)

Warrington, John
w. m. also clocks
136 South Front St. 1811 (D)–1817 (D)
inquire 1 South Front St. 1818 (D)
S.E. cor. Front & Chestnut Sts.
1819 (D)–1822 (D)
58 High St. 1831 (D)–1833 (D)

Warrington, John & S. R.
c. & w. ms.
96 High St. 1822 (D)
58 High St. 1823 (D)–1825 (D)

Warrington, John & Co.
c. & w. ms.
58 High St. 1828 (D)–1833 (D)

Warrington, S. R. & Co.
watches & clocks
58 High St. 1841 (D)–1850 (D)

Warrington, Samuel R.
c. & w. m.
6 Church Alley 1828 (D), 1829 (D)
58 Market St. 1831 (D)–1850 (D)

Watson, James
c. & w. m.
58 High St. 1821 (D), 1822 (D)
72 High St. 1823 (D)–1849 (D)
143 High St. 1850 (D)

Watson & Hildeburn
importers watches, jewelry & fine cutlery
72 High St. 1839 (D)–1849 (D)

Weatherly, David
c. & w. m.
29 Pewter Platter Alley 1805 (D)
87 North Third St. 1806 (D)
83 North Third St. 1807 (D), 1808 (D)
81 North Third St. 1809 (D)–1840 (D)
150 North Tenth St. 1840 (D)–1850 (D)

West, Josiah
c. & w. m.
12 Strawberry St. 1798 (D)
George near Eleventh St.
1807 (D), 1808 (D)

West, Thos. G.
c. & w. m.
13 North Third St. 1819 (D)–1822 (D)

West, James L.
jeweler
1 Carter's Alley 1829 (D)–1831 (D)
7 Penn St. 1833 (D)

Westphall, Charles W.
watchcase maker & jeweler
268 North Second St. 1822 (D)

Westphall, Ferdinand
watchcase maker & jeweler
11 York Court 1822 (D)
131 North Fourth St. 1823 (D), 1824 (D)

White, Joseph
c. & w. m.
162 North Third St. 1808 (D)–1811 (D)
3 Callowhill St. 1813 (D), 1814 (D)
153 St. John St. 1816 (D), 1817 (D)
Petticoat Alley 1818 (D)

White, Sebastian
w. m.
149 North Second St. 1795 (D), 1796 (D)

White, Thomas
c. & w. m.
44 North Seventh St. 1810 (D)

Whitehead, John
c. m.
Nectarine below 11th St.
1848 (D), 1849 (D)

Whitehead, Wm. G.
c. m.
Tenth above Pleasant St. 1850 (D)

Widdifield, William
92 North Fifth St. 1816 (D)
1 North Fifth St. 1817 (D)

Widdifield, William, Jr.
c. & w. m.
97 South Eighth St. 1821 (D), 1822 (D)

Widdifield & Gaw
c. & w. m.
449 North Second St.   1821 (D), 1822 (D)

Wiggins, Thomas & Co.
w. ms.
88 High St.   1833 (D)

Wilder, L. H. & Co.
clock dealers
104 North Third St.   1845 (D)

Wills, Joseph
c. m.
Born about 1700, died 1759.
During latter part of his life Joseph Wills lived on Third St. south of Mulberry (Arch) St. There is no evidence that Joseph Wills left any children.

Wilson, Robert
c. m.
23 Old Fourth St.   1835 (D), 1836 (D)

Winters, Isaac
w. m.
410 North Second St.   1844 (D)–1845 (D)
173 North Second St.   1845 (D)–1848 (D)

Witt, Dr. Christopher
Born Wiltshire, England, 1675, died Germantown 1765.
Dr. Witt (or De Witt) came to America in 1704. He was a physician who had delved in the occult and practical astronomy. In June 1691, a group of German Pietists came to Germantown. Kelpius was the leader. After two months they retired to the caves along the Wissahickon. When Witt came to America he at once joined this group of mystics. In 1706 he painted a portrait of Kelpius which is today probably the first portrait in oils done in America. Shortly after the death of Kelpius in 1708, at the age of 35, Witt moved into a small house in Germantown. Witt was a man of many sides. In the field of astronomy he described the great comet of 1743. He made an eight-foot telescope for his observations. He practiced horoscopy and cast nativities according to the positions of the heavenly bodies. So famous did he become in this field that he was known as *Hexmeister*—master of spells. When long winters made the study of botany in the fields impossible, Witt turned to clockmaking. At first he made "wand-uhren"—with long pendulums, weights of fifteen to twenty pounds and chains. These clocks were the forerunners of the tall case clock. Later he made tall case clocks. When Witt died at the age of ninety he was the last survivor of the Theosophical group that had dwelled in the caves of the Wissahickon.

Wood, John, Sr.
w. & c. m.
Died 1761.
The label of John Wood, Sr., reads: "Clocks, watches, gold and silver work made and mended at the sign of the dial, corner Front & Chestnut Sts." In 1734 Francis Richardson, outstanding silversmith, engraved five clock faces for John Wood. John Wood is said to have advertised in 1734.

Wood, John, Jr.
Born 1736, died 1793.
clockmaker and successful merchant.
Advertised extensively in English and German newspapers between 1760 and 1793.
Cor. Front & Chestnut Sts.   1785 (D)
55 South Front St.   1791 (D)

The Woolworth family of jewelers and clock dealers
Richard C. Woolworth
jeweler, c. & w. m.
72 High St.   1816 (D)–1817 (D)
69 Chestnut St.   1822 (D)
Hartung's Alley   1823 (D), 1824 (D)

Danforth Woolworth
jeweler
4 Hartung's Alley   1823 (D), 1824 (D)

Charles Woolworth
jeweler
35 Cherry St.   1829 (D)

Richard Woolworth
jeweler
35 Cherry St.   1831 (D)
161 Pine St.   1839 (D)

Y

Z

Yeager, William
  w. m.
  15 North Front St.   1837 (D)

Zeissler, G. A.
  c. m.
  Apple above George St.   1848 (D)

CLOCK AND WATCHMAKERS
OF PENNSYLVANIA

OUTSIDE OF PHILADELPHIA

THE COUNTIES OF PENNSYLVANIA

THE original royal grant to William Penn was for 40,000 square miles. The Commonwealth of Pennsylvania today covers 45,126 square miles.

Three counties were set up by Penn: Philadelphia County; Bucks County (named for Buckinghamshire, England, the ancestral home of Penn), and Chester County, named for Chester, England.

As the population increased and pushed westward, new counties were set up. Lancaster County, formed in 1729, was named for Lancashire, England; York County, formed in 1749, was named for the House of York; Cumberland County, formed in 1750, was named for the county of like name in England.

Northampton County was formed in 1752; Berks County, named for Berkshire, England, where the Penn family had large estates, was formed in the same year.

Bedford County, when formed in 1771, embraced the entire southwestern part of the Province. Northumberland, formed in 1772, was named for the Duke of Northumberland; Westmoreland, formed in 1771, was named for the English county of the same name.

After the Revolution additional counties were formed but no longer were they given names borrowed from England. Washington County, formed in 1781, was originally part of Augusta County in Virginia. Fayette County, formed in 1783, was named for Lafayette. Franklin County was formed in 1784, and in the same year Montgomery County, named for General Richard Montgomery, was set up. Dauphin County, named for the Dauphin of France, was formed in 1784. Luzerne County, formed in 1786, was named for the Chevalier de la Luzerne, French minister to the United States from 1779 to 1783.

It was not until the formation of Lackawanna County in 1878 that county lines were definitely settled. Pennsylvania now has 47 counties, many of which were formed by taking parts of counties previously set up.

In the place names of the clockmakers of Pennsylvania the present county locations are given.

CLOCKMAKERS OF PENNSYLVANIA

OUTSIDE OF PHILADELPHIA

A

Allebach, Henry　　　　　　　Reading
Advertised in German language newspaper in 1829.

André, John A.　　　　　　　Pottstown
　　　　　　　　　　　Montgomery Co.
clockmaker, watchmaker, dentist and politician.
Served in council (Pottstown) 1862–1863.
Burgess (Pottstown) 1864–1868.
Borough Treasurer 1869–1873.
Died October 18, 1880.

Andreas, Abraham　　　　　　Bethlehem
Born: Frederickstown, Montgomery Co., Pa., 1725, died, 1802.
Was originally a millwright but learned clockmaking. Came to Bethlehem in 1736. Married stepdaughter of Boemper. Succeeded Boemper in business in 1793.

Andreas, Henry　　　　　　　Bethlehem
Second son of Abraham Andreas.
Born 1762, died 1802.
Learned watchmaking in Philadelphia and moved to Bethlehem in 1800.

Atkinson, Wilmer　　　　　　Lancaster
Atkinson began as a cutler and seems to have come to Lancaster from Baltimore about 1748. He married the eldest daughter of Abraham Leroy, and husband and wife carried on the business of clock and watch repairing. Although Atkinson was not a clockmaker himself, his name appears on at least one very fine clock, which evidently was made by his wife.

Avis, M.　　　　　　　　　　Reading
Advertised in 1827.

B

Bachman, John　　　　　　Bachmanville
　　　　　　　　　　　　　Lancaster Co.
Born 1798. Was cabinet maker, and although he sold clocks under his own name he made no pretense at making them. He made cases for Joseph Bowman of Strasburg, and Anthony W. Baldwin of Lampeter. His custom was to make two cases for one set of works completed as his fee. Then he would make a case for this set of works and sell the third clock on his own account.

Bakewell, John P.　　　　　　Pittsburgh
Son of Benjamin Bakewell, who was among Pittsburgh's earliest glass manufacturers. Oct. 1, 1830, a patent was issued to John P. Bakewell for glass wheels for clocks.

Baldwin, Anthony Wayne　Lampeter Square
　　　　　　　　　　　　　Lancaster Co.
Born in Newlin Township, Chester County, 1783. (Newlin Twp. is near the Lancaster Co. line.)
Died Lampeter Square, 1867.
Anthony Wayne Baldwin learned his trade in New Holland, with John Bowman, the father of Joseph Bowman. He married Maria Bowman, the oldest sister of Joseph Bowman. Started in business for himself in Lampeter Square in 1810.

Baldwin, John Charles　　　　Lancaster
The oldest son of Anthony W. Baldwin. Learned clockmaking with his father but soon abandoned this trade for public life. It is interesting to note, however, that John Charles Baldwin had much to do with bringing wholesale watchmaking to Lancaster as an industry and he was influenced in this by the fact that he was a clockmaker.

Baldwin, George W.　　　　Sadsburyville
　　　　　　　　　　　　　　Chester Co.
Born 1777, died about 1867.
Brother of Anthony W. Baldwin.
Active as a clockmaker between 1802 and 1844.

Beatty, George　　　　　　Harrisburg
Born in Ireland 1781, died in Harrisburg 1862.
Learned clockmaking with his brother-in-law Samuel Hill. Established his own business in 1808 and conducted it until 1862.

Beckel, Charles F.   Bethlehem
After serving apprenticeship with John Samuel Krause and Jedediah Weiss, Charles F. Beckel set up business in 1826 with Henry D. Bishop as his apprentice. Bishop assumed business in 1830 when Charles F. Beckel built an iron foundry.

Benedict, Philip   Lancaster
Born 1771, died 1862.
Primarily a stove maker and worker in metal. Made one crude but unusual clock.

Bentley, Eli   West Whiteland Twp.
Chester Co.
Resided and worked in West Whiteland Township in 1774, 1775, 1776, and 1778, in which years he was taxed in the township. In 1783 he was residing in Maryland with his wife at Taneytown. He evidently later moved to Virginia, according to a deed dated Oct. 7, 1791.

Bevans, William   Norristown
Montgomery Co.
Born 1755, died 1819.
Came to Norristown from Philadelphia and advertised in Norristown newspapers in 1816, four years after town was incorporated.

Bishop, Henry D.   Bethlehem
Assumed Charles F. Beckel's business in 1830.

Bishop, Moritz   Easton
Was in business in Easton in 1786 and for many years thereafter.

The Bixler family
This family started as clockmakers with Christian Bixler (1732–1811), who worked in Reading, Pa., until 1790. His son, also named Christian, went to Easton, Pa., and started a business which remained in the Bixler family in a direct male line for more than 160 years.

Christian Bixler   Reading
Born in Lancaster of Swiss parentage in 1732. He was a clockmaker in Reading between 1750 and 1790. He died in 1811.

Christian Bixler, Jr.   Easton
Born in Robeson Township, Berks County, June 1763.
Served his apprenticeship under John Keim, of Reading, learning clockmaking and silversmithing. Leaving his master in 1785 he set himself up in business in Easton, Pa., then a very small town at the junction of the Delaware and Lehigh rivers. Christian Bixler, Jr., was active in business and affairs in Easton from 1785 to 1830.

Daniel Bixler   Easton
Son of Christian Bixler, Jr.
In about 1827 ground was broken for the canal system which was to make Easton an important city. In addition to this commercial importance, Lafayette College, which had been chartered in 1826, moved into its present group of buildings in Easton in 1834. The Bixler business, which had been taken over by Daniel, shared in this prosperity.

C. Willis Bixler   Easton
Son of Daniel Bixler.
C. Willis Bixler was proprietor of the business which had turned from clockmaking to jewelry, in which business it operated for many years.

Arthur B. Bixler   Easton
The son of C. Willis Bixler was born in 1882 and died in 1945. He was the last in the male line of six generations of clockmakers and jewelers.

Blumer, Jacob   Allentown
Born in Whitehall Township 1774, died 1830.
Clockmaker from about 1798 to 1820.
Lieutenant, War of 1812.

Boemper, Abraham   Bethlehem
Born 1705 in Nassau, died 1793.
Learned his profession of clockmaking in Marburg; after short residence in Holland went to South America, thence to New York, where he became business manager of the Moravian Church. After death of his first wife he went to Bethlehem and in 1748 married the widow of Isaac Martens Ysselsteyn. Boemper evidently set himself up in business in Bethlehem at time of his second marriage.

Borneman, Henry H.   Boyertown
Berks Co.
Was in business of making and repairing

clocks in Boyertown as early as 1840, and remained in business until his death prior to 1890.

Borneman, Joseph H.   Boyertown
Berks Co.
Was apprenticed to Henry H. Borneman in about 1850.

Bowman, Joseph   Strasburg
Lancaster Co.
Born New Holland, Lancaster Co., 1799, died 1892.
At the age of ten he moved to Lampeter Township with his father, who was a clockmaker. At 17 he was apprenticed to his brother-in-law Anthony Wayne Baldwin. In Dec. 1820, having finished his trade, he married and set up in business for himself in Strasburg Borough, where he lived for the rest of his long life. He carried on his business for 53 years but does not seem to have made many clocks after 1850. ·

Bowman, John   New Holland
(Also spelled Bauman.)   Lancaster Co.
The father of Joseph Bowman. About 1809 John Bowman moved from New Holland to Lampeter Township and seems to have then given up clockmaking for farming.

Boyer, Jacob   Boyertown
Berks Co.
Born 1754, died 1796.
Father of the founders of Boyertown. He originally came from Frederick Township in Montgomery County. There is one clock known marked by his name.

Boyter, Daniel   Lancaster
Advertised in Lancaster Journal, Nov. 1, 1805:
"Begs leave to inform the public that he occupies the stand next to the stage office, E. King St., and solicits the favor of . . . Repeating and common watches, clocks and timepieces, carefully repaired on short notice and at the lowest prices." Daniel Boyter advertised that he was "late from England."

Brant, Adam   New Hanover
Montgomery Co.
This man was a prolific clockmaker of Montgomery County. It has been impos-

sible to ascertain the exact dates of his birth and death. A very careful survey has failed to disclose an Adam Brant clock with a brass dial, hence it must be assumed that he worked during and shortly after the Revolution, when the painted dial was used. The painted dials of Adam Brant's clocks are all very well done. His clocks show a high degree of skill in workmanship.

Brenneisen, Samuel   Reading and
Adamstown
Lancaster Co.
(Also spelled Breneiser.)
Advertised in Reading in 1799. Moved to Adamstown between 1807 and 1810. Made a great many clocks.

Brenneisen, George   Womelsdorf
Berks Co.
Brother of Samuel Brenneisen and contemporary with him.

Burrowes, Thomas   Strasburg
Lancaster Co.
Born in Ireland. First came to Delaware in 1784 and to Lancaster Co. in 1787.
Had been educated for the Episcopal ministry in Ireland but never took holy orders. Engaged in clockmaking in Strasburg from 1787 to 1810. Returned to Ireland in 1810 to collect a legacy but came back to Strasburg in 1822. Died in 1839.

C

Carpenter, Anthony   New Holland
Lancaster Co.
Born near New Holland in 1790, died 1868.
Began business in New Holland in 1820.

Carpenter, A. W.   New Holland
Lancaster Co.
Born 1814, died 1869.
Son of Anthony Carpenter. Succeeded his father in business in about 1830 and continued until 1860.

Cave, Joseph   West Goshen Twp.
and West Chester
Chester Co.
Born in the 1790's, died about 1847.
Clocks marked West Goshen were made

after 1817. Joseph Cave advertised in West Chester in 1821. Was in Philadelphia late in his life.

The Chandlee family
Benjamin Chandlee Nottingham, on boundary line between Chester Co., Pennsylvania, and Cecil Co., Maryland
Born in Ireland 1685, died 1745.
Came to Philadelphia at age of 17. Married Sarah Cottey. Moved to Nottingham 1711–12. Gave up clockmaking at Nottingham in 1741.

Benjamin Chandlee Nottingham
Born 1723, died 1791.
Son of Benjamin Chandlee (the elder) and Sarah Cottey. Took over father's business in 1741. Married Mary Folwell in 1749 and had four sons.

Ellis Chandlee Nottingham
Born 1755, died 1815.
Son of Benjamin Chandlee, Jr., and Mary Folwell. Took over father's business in 1791 at his father's death.

Isaac Chandlee Nottingham
Born 1760, died 1813.
Son of Benjamin Chandlee, Jr., and Mary Folwell. Isaac worked under Ellis after their father's death in 1791. Some clocks bear the inscription "Ellis & Isaac Chandlee," while others are marked "Isaac Chandlee."

Goldsmith Chandlee Stephensburg and Winchester, Virginia
Born 1751, died 1821.
Son of Benjamin Chandlee, Jr., and Mary Folwell. Served apprenticeship under his father and went to Virginia in 1775.

John Chandlee Wilmington Delaware
Born 1757, died 1813.
Son of Benjamin Chandlee, Jr., and Mary Folwell. Was in business in Wilmington from 1795 to 1810.

Goldsmith Chandlee, Jr. Winchester, Virginia
The son of Goldsmith Chandlee, Sr. Upon his father's death in 1821 he continued his

father's business in Winchester until 1830 when he went west to Ohio.

Benjamin Chandlee Baltimore, Maryland
The son of Goldsmith Chandlee, Sr. Was watch- and clockmaker in Baltimore from 1814 to 1818. From 1818 to 1823 was in partnership with Robert Halloway under the firm name of Chandlee and Halloway.

Chester, Richard York
Born c. 1770, died 1816.
Clock- and watchmaker. Son of English schoolmaster and later tavern keeper. A number of clocks marked "Richard Chester" are in existence, both 30-hour and eight-day type.

Christ, Daniel Kutztown Berks Co.
This man made clocks in the late 18th and early 19th centuries.

Cochran, George Goshen Twp. and West Chester Chester Co.
Watchmaker. Was evidently in business when West Chester was incorporated as a borough in 1799.

Conlyn, Thomas Carlisle Cumberland Co.
Thomas Conlyn founded the Conlyn Jewelry Store in Carlisle in 1839. He never made watches or clocks, but his label may be found in watches and clocks that he sold and repaired. He served his apprenticeship with Charles Canby of Wilmington, Del.

Cooke, Alexander Canonsburg Washington Co.
Canonsburg, situated on Chartiers Creek about 17 miles from Pittsburgh, was settled by John Canon in 1773, laid out as a town in 1786, and set up as a borough in 1802. Alexander Cooke, the clockmaker, was among the taxables when the borough was set up.

Cope, John Lancaster
Born Nov. 14, 1763, the son of Caleb Cope, burgess of Lancaster when Major André

was captured and sent to Lancaster with other British prisoners of war. Major André lived in Caleb Cope's home. There is one John Cope clock known, with the word Lancaster and "No. 4" under the date window. John Cope was an apprentice of David Rittenhouse and later had a machine shop in West Chester.

Corl, Abraham   East Nantmeal Twp.
"Coventry"
Chester Co.
Born 1779, died 1842.
Was well established as a clockmaker in 1808. After death of his wife he moved to Coventryville, a settlement near East Nantmeal, and clocks made there are marked "Coventry."

Custer, Jacob D.   Norristown
Montgomery Co.
Born 1805, died 1872.
Self-taught, having had only 6 weeks' schooling. In his 19th year he set up as a clock- and watchmaker between Shannonville and Jeffersonville in Montgomery County. Moved to Norristown in 1832 and soon began to make steeple clocks. In 1834 he made the clock for the county court house. Made town clocks for Uniontown, Danville, Gettysburg and Phoenixville in Pennsylvania; Salem, Ohio; Bridgeton, N. J.; as well as towns in South Carolina and Alabama. His best period was between 1840 and 1845. Made "fog bells" of his own invention for the government in 1850. He began the manufacture of tall case clocks in about 1831, and in 1842 commenced the manufacture of "clocks" to propel the lights of lighthouses for the government.

Custer, Isaac   Norristown
Montgomery Co.
Brother of Jacob D. Custer. Set up in business in Norristown, but left in 1837 or 1838 to go west.

D

Danner, Alexander   Lancaster
Made cases for clocks of the Shreiners, and hence was contemporary with them. Probably the finest clock case maker of Lancaster.

Darlington, Benedict   Westtown
Chester Co.
Born 1786, died 1864.
Member of a prominent Chester County family and a man of many parts—merchant and manufacturer. Shortly after War of 1812 Benedict Darlington engaged three men from Connecticut—Hatch, Dewolf and Vibber—to make clocks with wooden works which he sold around Chester County. It is possible that both the works and faces for these clocks came from Connecticut and that Benedict Darlington made the cases.

Davis, Gabriel   Manheim
Lancaster Co.
Clockmaker in 1780.

Davis, John   New Holland
Lancaster Co.
Listed in the returns for Earl Township, 1805–1807. Made clocks with enameled dials.

Davis, Phineas   York
Born 1795, died 1835.
Born in Grafton County, New Hampshire, and came to York when about 15 years old. He was apprenticed to the York clockmaker Jonathan Jessup and remained with him until he was of age. Shortly thereafter he formed a partnership with Isaac Gardner and they built the iron steamboat *Codorus* in 1828. In 1831 Phineas Davis built *The York*, the first coal-burning steam locomotive in the United States. In 1832 he left York to take charge of the Baltimore and Ohio Railroad shops in Baltimore. He was killed in a railroad accident in 1835.

Davis, Samuel   Pittsburgh
Listed as a clockmaker in 1815, 1819, and 1826.

Dickey, Thomas   Harrisburg
Dauphin Co.
Clockmaker in Marietta and later in Harrisburg. He is listed among the taxables of 1812–1814.

Diehl, Jacob   Reading
Berks Co.
Took over Daniel Rose's shop in 1798 in Rose's absence. Advertised in 1804.

Drawbaugh, Daniel   Eberly's Mills
Cumberland Co.

Born 1847, died 1911.

The son of a blacksmith, this man proved a prolific inventor and during his lifetime had some 125 patents issued to him. He preceded Bell with a workable telephone by ten years and this resulted in long-drawn-out litigation. Drawbaugh invented an electric clock and made three of them. One was exhibited in Harrisburg. The advertisement read: "Greatest piece of mechanism of the age. All should see the magnetic clock. Seven feet by two feet 3 inches. Pendulum weighs 25 pounds. Motive power is derived from the earth by means of two small metal plates buried in the ground to which two insulated wires are attached and ingeniously connected with the works of the clock." (Actually, Drawbaugh had made a large chemical battery in the soil.)

Dring, Thomas   West Chester
Chester Co.

Was working in West Chester when it was incorporated as a borough in 1799.

E

The Eberman family

The period of greatest activity of this distinguished family of clockmakers was from 1780 to 1820, although some of the sons were active to a later date.

John Eberman, the first clockmaker of that name and a man of importance, was born in 1749 and died in 1835.

He had three sons, all clockmakers:

John Eberman. Born 1776, died 1846.

Jacob Eberman. Born 1773, died 1837.

Joseph Eberman. Born 1780, died 1844.

Jacob Eberman made but few clocks, the John Ebermans, father and son, made many.

Charles Eberman, a son of Joseph Eberman, followed the business of watchmaker and jeweler.

Eby, Christian   Manheim
Lancaster Co.

Started in business in Manheim in 1830. The business was continued by his two sons, *George* and *Jacob Eby*, and was still in existence in 1860.

Ehst, David K.   Boyertown
Berks Co.

Was in business as early as 1840 in a one-story building. He was a man of education. Died about 1885.

Ellicott, Joseph   Buckingham
Bucks Co.

Born 1732, died 1780.

A man of great mechanical and mathematical ability. Joseph Ellicott lived in Bucks County, where he was born, until 1770. For a time he was high sheriff of the county. He made a trip to England in 1767 to collect an inheritance and upon his return began work on his masterpiece—a clock with four faces. This clock is still extant. In the making of this clock he was assisted by his son Andrew. The clock was finished in 1769. In 1770 Joseph Ellicott purchased a large tract of land in Maryland, about ten miles from Baltimore. This location was later known as Ellicott's Upper and Lower Mills. Here were built flour and cotton mills as well as an iron foundry. Joseph Ellicott made in all about 300 clocks while in Bucks County.

Ellicott, Andrew   Buckingham
Bucks Co.

Born 1754, died 1820.

Son of Joseph Ellicott.

Clock, watch and instrument maker. Was a very distinguished man and became surveyor general of the United States in 1792 and professor of mathematics at West Point in 1812.

Engle, Stephen D.   Hazelton
Luzerne Co.

Born 1837, died 1921.

His father was a watchmaker and jeweler. Stephen D. Engle was not only a clockmaker and inventor but also a dentist. He built the first astronomical, musical and apostolic clock in America, completing this masterpiece in 1877. For many years it was exhibited as a "theatrical" attraction.

Ely, Hugh   New Hope
Bucks Co.

Appeared in business in New Hope about 1800. Known to have made at least four clocks, one for the county almshouse.

Erb, John   Conestoga Centre
Lancaster Co.
Clockmaker and repairer.
In business in Conestoga Centre between about 1835 and 1860. At least one clock is known bearing his name.

Erwin, Edward F.   Bethlehem
Succeeded John M. Miksch at his death in 1882. Was still in business in 1892.

Esterlie, John   New Holland
Lancaster Co.
Born near Shamokin, Pa., in 1778. Was first in business in Lebanon, Pa., then came to New Holland. Returned to Lebanon but was soon back in New Holland, where he remained in business until he retired about 1830. His period of activity in New Holland was from about 1812 to 1830.

Evans, Septimus   Warwick
Bucks Co.
In business about 1810. Made several clocks.

F

Faber, George   Sumneytown
Montgomery Co.
Was making clocks in Sumneytown (spelled "Sunnytown" on some of his clocks) in 1773, and probably before. In 1773 he moved to Reading, some thirty miles away, where he worked for several years.

Fasig, Conrad   Reading
Worked in late 18th and early 19th centuries.

Fertig, Jacob   Vincent Twp.
Chester Co.
Born 1778, died 1823.
Worked in Chester County except for a short period while he was in Philadelphia. (See Jacob Fertig in Philadelphia section.)

Fiester, John   Lancaster
Born in 1846.
In 1878 John Fiester finished and exhibited an "apostolic clock" upon which he had spent eleven years of labor. He traveled from town to town exhibiting the clock in a wagon. While in Manheim, Lancaster County, he was befriended by George H.

Danner, the great collector of clocks, and Fiester gave Mr. Danner this clock as payment. The clock is now part of the Danner Collection in the Hershey Museum, Hershey, Pennsylvania.

Fisher, John   York
One of the most prominent of York's clockmakers and among the first. "Johannes Fischer" was born in Germany and arrived in Philadelphia in 1749. He accompanied his parents and sister. The parents died a few days apart, presumably in a fever epidemic. Little is known of Fisher's first ten years in America, but he appeared in York in 1759. He achieved a large measure of success as a clockmaker, carver in wood, and painter of portraits. He married and at his death was a man of means. He is buried in Zion Lutheran Cemetery, York. His masterpiece is the astronomical clock now the property of Yale University.

Fix, George   Reading
Berks Co.
Mentioned as a clockmaker in 1802.

Fix, Joseph   Reading
Berks Co.
Early 19th century. Advertised in 1829 that he had equipment to cut clock wheels.

Ford, George   Lancaster
Died 1842. Period of activity 1811 to 1840. Also made surveyor's and nautical instruments.
Upon his death his son, also George Ford, inherited the business and conducted it for a short time.

Forrer, Christian   Lampeter
Lancaster Co.
Born in Switzerland 1737.
Came to Lancaster County in 1754.
In 1774 moved to Newberry Township, York County.
Died 1783.

Fraser, William   New Ephrata, now Lincoln
Lancaster Co.
Born in Philadelphia 1801, died 1877.
Apprentice in large clock manufactory of Solomon Park in Philadelphia 1814–1821. Came to New Holland in 1828, working for Carpenter and Esterlie. Finally started in business for himself in Lincoln. This busi-

ness was acquired by his son William Fraser, and then in turn by his grandsons Samuel K. Fraser and William K. Fraser.

Freytit, Peter   Pittsburgh
Clock and watchmaker in Diamond Alley 1813 to 1837 (D).

Friend, Frederick   Pittsburgh
Clock- and watchmaker in Diamond Alley 1813 to 1837 (D).

G

Gaillard, Peter   Reading
Advertised in 1794. Came from France.

Garrett, Benjamin   Goshen
                                Chester Co.
Born 1771, died 1856. A prolific and excellent clockmaker of Chester County who seems to have made his own cases. His period of productivity seems to have been before 1817.

Geiger, Jacob   Allentown
                                 Lehigh Co.
Was a clockmaker in Allentown in 1787, but moved to Maryland.

Gifft, Peter   Kutztown
                                  Berks Co.
Late 18th and early 19th centuries.

Godschalk, Jacob   Towamencin Twp.
                          Montgomery Co.
                                    and
                            Philadelphia
A famous pre-Revolutionary clockmaker. Contemporary of David Rittenhouse and a native of Towamencin Township (then Philadelphia County but now Montgomery). His earlier clocks bear the title "Jacob Godschalk, Towamencin." In the late 1760s Jacob Godschalk moved from Towamencin to the City of Philadelphia. The Philadelphia tax lists of 1769 list him as a resident of Mulberry Ward, East Part. His shop was on Arch Street between Second and Third. He is mentioned as a clockmaker in the 1774 tax list and as a watchmaker in 1780. After coming to Philadelphia he marked some of his clocks "Jacob Godshalk," dropping the German *sch*. Jacob Godschalk married Elizabeth

Owen in Dec. 1770. She was probably a widow with a son Griffith, since in April 1773 Griffith Owen, who later became a famous clockmaker himself, was apprenticed to Jacob Godschalk. The apprenticeship ended in 1780. Jacob Godschalk paid taxes in Philadelphia for the last time in 1781 and evidently died soon after. He was a member of the Fishing Company of Fort St. Davids and a lieutenant in the Revolutionary War.

Goodhart, Jacob   Lebanon
(also spelled Guthart)   Lebanon Co.
Came from Reading, Pa., and succeeded Jacob Graf as clockmaker. Many clocks in the vicinity bear his name. Was first representative of county in legislature when Lebanon became a separate county in 1813, serving three terms until 1818. Was the first burgess when Lebanon became a borough in 1821, and served as county treasurer 1826–1829.

The Gorgas family of Lancaster County
Jacob Gorgas   Ephrata
                             Lancaster Co.
Born in Germantown (Philadelphia) in 1728. Died at Ephrata in 1798 and is buried in the cemetery of Ephrata Cloisters. Came from a distinguished family and was a first cousin of David Rittenhouse. In 1763 he was living in Ephrata and married. He made about 150 clocks, mostly marked "Ephrata."

Solomon Gorgas   Ephrata
                             Lancaster Co.
Born 1764, died 1838. Son of Jacob Gorgas, he continued his father's business together with his brother Joseph, after father's death in 1798. In 1800 Solomon Gorgas purchased a large tract of land in Cumberland County, west of Harrisburg, and apparently then abandoned clockmaking. At least one clock is known marked "Solomon Gorgas."

Joseph Gorgas   Ephrata
                             Lancaster Co.
Born 1770. Son of Jacob Gorgas, he continued business with his brother Solomon after father's death. In 1806 he moved from Ephrata to Running Pumps, near Elizabethtown, and is supposed to have con-

tinued making clocks. No clocks bearing the name of Joseph Gorgas have been found.

Govett, George
Norristown
Montgomery Co.
and later
Philadelphia

Son-in-law of William Bevens, George Govett came from Philadelphia and continued the Bevens business from 1819 to 1831 in Norristown.
In Philadelphia from 1814 (D) to 1819 (D)
Corner High & Front Sts.   1814 (D)
26 North Seventh St.   1818 (D) to 1820(D)
In Philadelphia after leaving Norristown.
21 South Tenth St.   1841 (D)–1842 (D)
49 South Tenth St.   1943 (D) to 1850 (D)

Graf, Jacob
Lebanon
Lebanon Co.

Probably the earliest clockmaker in Lebanon. There is extant a clock marked "1735 —Jacob Graf—in Lebanon."
In 1750 Lebanon Township—embracing the town of Lebanon—contained nearly 130 taxables. Among these was Jacob Graf, clockmaker.

Graff, Joseph
Allentown
Lehigh Co.

Partner with Jacob Blumer for a few years but soon moved to Maryland. Clock is known dated 1799 carrying names of Jacob Blumer and Joseph Graff.

Graves, Alfred
Willow Grove
Montgomery Co.

Son of a great Sheffield cutler, made clocks in Willow Grove about 1845.

Greer, John
Carlisle
Cumberland Co.

Watchmaker. Died in 1774.

Grim, George
Orwigsburg
Berks Co.

Born about 1792.
George Grim was a prominent Mason in Orwigsburg and this fact is reflected in the decorations of his clocks, since they usually bear Masonic devices.
Orwigsburg was founded by Peter Orwig in 1795.

Orwigsburg Academy was chartered in 1813.
The Court House was erected in 1815, the second story being used for Masonic meetings.
George Grim was a trustee of the Academy and was initiated into Schuylkill Lodge No. 138, F. & A. M., Feb. 2, 1819. He was 27 at the time.

Grosh, Peter Lehn
Lancaster

A portrait painter allied to clockmaking who advertised in 1830 "clock faces manufactured and painted to order."

Gulick, Nathan
Easton

Worked in Easton about 1790 and made very fine clocks.

Gunkle, John
Trout Run
Cocalico Twp.
Lancaster Co.

Also spelled his name Kunkle.
A German by birth, whose period of activity was from about 1830 to 1840. Made few clocks but excellent ones.

H

Hahn, Henry
Reading

Born 1754, died 1843.
His period of activity seems to have been from about 1790 to about 1820.

Hall, Christian
Lititz
Lancaster Co.

Born in Bethlehem in 1775, died in Lititz in 1848.
Began business in Lititz in early 1800s and retired about 1830.

Hall, Henry William
Lititz
Lancaster Co.

Born 1809, died 1868.
The son of Christian Hall, he continued his father's business.

Hall, John
West Chester
Chester Co.

Born 1793, died 1867.
His period of activity as a clockmaker was probably before 1825, but he continued very busy as a repairer.

Haller, Jacob   Aaronsburg
                                   Center Co.
Appeared on Haines Township tax list in
1810. There are several clocks extant made
by this man.

Heebner, David S.   Worcester Twp.
                           Montgomery Co.
Born 1810, died 1888.
The son of Rev. Balthasar Heebner, a
Schwenckfeldian minister. Upon reaching
manhood his father established David S.
Heebner on a farm, but the son, being of
an inventive turn of mind, soon turned to
clockmaking, at which he was very successful. In 1840 David S. Heebner opened
a shop for making farm machinery, and his
firm became very well known.

Heffley, Annanias   Berlin
                                   Somerset Co.
Born 1817, died 1876.
Annanias Heffley made the same kind of
clocks as Daniel Heffley, in Berlin, and
worked about the same time. His clocks
bear his name on the dial.

Heffley, Daniel   Berlin
                                   Somerset Co.
Born 1813, died 1887.
Was apprentice to Samuel Hoffard. Continued to make clocks, which bear his name
until 1867.

Heintzelman, John Conrad   Manheim
                               Lancaster Co.
Born 1766, died 1804.
Flourished in latter 18th century. Had a
son Peter who continued the business for a
short time after his father's death.

Heisely, George J.   Harrisburg
Born in Frederick, Maryland, in 1789,
died in Harrisburg in 1880.
Clock and surveyor instrument maker.
Family moved to Harrisburg in 1811 and
George J. Heisely was in business at Sec-
ond & Walnut streets. Besides being a
clockmaker, George J. Heisely was a flute
player. There is a family tradition that
George J. Heisely was the man who picked
the tune of "To Anacreon in Heaven" for
the "Star-spangled Banner." He joined
Capt. Thomas Walker's Company, First
Regiment, First Brigade, Pennsylvania Mi-

litia. On the roster of this company will
also be found the names of Ferdinand and
George Durang. This company marched
to the defense of Baltimore. Francis Scott
Key had written his stirring verses after
the bombardment of Fort McHenry on a
September night in 1814. A copy of the
verses reached the camp of the Pennsylvania militia, and the Durang brothers en-
listed the aid of Heisely to set the verses to
music. He played through his "tune book,"
and "To Anacreon in Heaven" was chosen.
Shortly afterwards, when the company
went on to Baltimore, the Durang brothers
sang the patriotic anthem to this tune on
the stage of the Holliday Street Theatre.
The town clock in Waynesburg, Greene
County, Pennsylvania, was made by
George J. Heisely.

Heisley, Frederick   Lancaster
Born in Lancaster in 1759, died in Harrisburg in 1839.
Served in the Revolution and then was in
business in Frederick, Maryland, from 1783
to 1793 as an instrument maker. Married a
daughter of George Hoff and in 1793 entered a partnership with George Hoff
which lasted for about eight years. Then
moved to Harrisburg, where he was treasurer of Dauphin County for a time.

Hendel, Bernard   Carlisle
                               Cumberland Co.
Conducted a jewelry store and advertised
himself as a clock- and watchmaker in first
quarter of the 19th century. It seems that
Bernard Hendel made clock cases that carried his name but that the movements were
constructed elsewhere.

Hendel, Jacob   Carlisle
                               Cumberland Co.
Brother of Bernard Hendel, he used the
same advertising, but there is a question
whether they were associated in business.

Hibbard, Caleb   Willistown
                               Chester Co.
Born 1781, died in Ohio in 1835.
An excellent clockmaker who made practically all his clocks in Chester County before leaving for Ohio in the winter of
1818–1819.

Hill, Benjamin   Richmond Twp.
Berks Co.

Died 1809.
Worked in late 18th century up to his death. He made the clock for the second court house in Reading, and there is a tradition that it stopped when he died, never to run again.

Hill, Arundel   Richmond Twp.
Berks Co.

The son of Benjamin Hill. Succeeded his father upon the latter's death in 1809.

Hill, Samuel   Harrisburg
Born in England 1765, died 1809.
He learned his trade in London and was in business in Dauphin County in 1785. Maintained his business until 1794. In 1790 Samuel Hill married Nancy Beatty and taught her youngest brother, George Beatty, his trade.

The Hoff family of Lancaster
George Hoff   Lancaster
Born in Westerberg, Germany, about 1740, died 1816. Came to America 1765. George Hoff settled in Lancaster shortly after coming to America. In Dec. 1769 he bought a property on West King Street, Lancaster, and thereafter until their deaths George Hoff and his son John Hoff followed clockmaking.

John Hoff   Lancaster
Son of George Hoff.
Died 1819.
It is not apparent just when John Hoff took over his father's business, but he worked with him and for him for years and was with him when the father died. However, for a short period in 1800 John Hoff was in the clockmaking business in Lancaster for himself.

Mrs. John Hoff   Lancaster
Wife of John Hoff.
Died 1822.
After her husband's death the widow of John Hoff "procured good workmen from Philadelphia" and carried on her late husband's clockmaking business. She also sold bonnets.

Hoffard, Samuel   Berlin
Somerset Co.

Born 1801, died 1845.
Made the same kind of clocks as those made by Michael Hugus at Berlin, Somerset County.

Hollenbach, David   Reading
Advertised in 1826 that he had just established himself in business after working for Daniel Oyster for four years.

Hollingshead, Job   Newtown
Bucks Co.

Advertised as clock- and watchmaker in 1821.

Hostetter, Jacob   Hanover
York Co.

Born 1754, died 1831.
A pioneer clockmaker of York County. He produced his first clock in 1798 after learning the trade from Richard Chester, the first clockmaker in Hanover, York County. Jacob Hostetter was also a politician, member of the state legislature, and a member of Congress (1818–1821). In 1825 he moved to Ohio and set up a clockmaking business with his son in the colony around New Lisbon.

Huber, Christian   Cocalico Twp.
Lancaster Co.

Died 1789.

Hugus, Michael   Berlin
Somerset Co.

Born in Northampton Co., Pa., in 1775, died 1825.
John Hugus, father of Michael, was born in the French colony near Hasse Cassel, Germany, in 1745, of Huguenot parents. John Hugus came to America in 1761, and when Michael was 12 years of age the family moved to Westmoreland County. The original name of the family was Hugo, and there is a connection between Victor Hugo, the French writer, and the American Hugus family.

Humphrey, Joshua   Charlestown and
East Whiteland
Chester Co.

Born 1744.
This Chester County clockmaker must not be confused with Joshua Humphrey, the

naval architect. Joshua Humphrey, the clockmaker, first appears in Chester Co. tax lists in 1764 and moved from the county in about 1773 to the "western liberties" of Philadelphia.

J

Jackson, Isaac London Grove and
New Garden
Chester Co.
Born 1734, died 1807.
A prominent Chester County clockmaker and maker of excellent clocks.

Jackson, George Unionville
East Marlborough Twp.
Chester Co.
Born before 1778, died in Wilmington, Del., 1836.
His period of activity in Chester County was between 1798 and 1812. Probably made many clocks upon which he did not place his name.

Jackson, John East Marlborough Twp.
Chester Co.
Born 1746, died in Baltimore, Md., 1795.
First cousin of Isaac Jackson.
John Jackson was a Tory and a rather difficult character throughout his life. It appears that he joined a colony of Loyalists from Chester County in New Brunswick and Nova Scotia for a while in 1787.

Jameson, Jacob Columbia
Lancaster Co.
Opened a clockmaking and watch-repair shop in 1818. In 1823 moved to Dayton, Ohio, where he died about 1830.

Jefferis, Curtis West Chester
Chester Co.
Born 1785.
Left West Chester about 1819.
Clock- and watchmaker and silversmith.

Jessop, Jonathan Yorktown
York Co.
Born 1771, died 1857.
Came to York with his mother when thirteen years old and was apprenticed to Elisha Kirk, a cousin of his mother, to learn clock- and watchmaking. He was a man of great mechanical skill and his clocks became famous. In addition to this he was an engineer of repute and engaged in the construction of many public works. He built a section of the Washington branch of the Baltimore and Ohio Railroad, and a station, "Jessop's," was named for him. Among his many endeavors was a mill for the manufacture of cotton cloth. In addition to all this he developed and perfected the York Imperial apple on his farm near York. He was a founding director of the York National Bank and one of the early presidents of the Vigilant Fire Company. Despite his great activity and many interests he retained his love for clock- and watchmaking and repaired a watch the day before he died.

Jessop, Joseph Updegraff
Born 1796, died 1859.
The eldest son of Jonathan Jessop. Was associated with his father in the clockmaking business and gradually took over this business as his father busied himself with road construction and other enterprises. Joseph Jessop never married.

K

Keim, John Reading
Born 1749, died 1819.
Was established in the clock trade as early as 1779. He was prominent in city and county affairs as well as in clockmaking.

Kennedy, Elisha Easton
Clockmaker in Easton in 1786 and 1787.

Kessler, John Reading
Watchmaker listed in Directory of 1806–1807.

Kirk, Elisha York
Born 1757, died 1790.
Clockmaker and pewterer.
Son of Chester County Quakers who came to York in 1770. In 1774 Elisha Kirk returned to New Garden, Chester County, where he lived with Isaac Jackson, under whom he learned his trade, until 1780. He returned to York and lived there for the rest of his life. Two clocks are known: the one marked "Elisha Kirk No. 67 and Jonathan Jessop No. 1," and the other, a 30 hour clock, is marked No. 95. Upon his death Elisha Kirk willed his clockmaking tools to his son Aquilla.

Klingman, Jacob   Reading
Died 1806.
Signed his clocks Jacob Kling. Clock made
by him now in the Woman's Club of Reading bears date 1776.

Kohl, Nicholas   Willow Grove
                              Montgomery Co.
Made a number of tall case clocks in about
1830.

Kopolan, Washington   Norristown
(Also spelled Koplin.)   Montgomery Co.
Was in business in Norristown in 1850.

Krause, John Samuel   Bethlehem
Born in Christianbrunn in 1782, died 1815.
Came to Bethlehem to learn clockmaking
with John George Weiss in 1797, and in
1803 went to Lancaster to perfect himself.
In 1810 he married Maria Louisa Schropp.
John Samuel Krause had three apprentices
—Jedediah Weiss, Charles F. Beckel, and
John M. Miksch.

Krauss, Samuel   Kraussdale
                          Upper Hanover Twp.
                            Montgomery Co.
Born 1807, died 1904.
A member of the famous Schwenckfeld
Krauss family of organ builders. In addition to being a clockmaker, he was a store-
keeper, inventor, foundryman, miller, and
farmer. At various times he was engaged in
business in Philadelphia, Upper Milford,
Upper Hanover, Allentown, and Coopers-
burg. In 1886 he retired from business and
moved to Sumneytown. He was in Upper
Milford and Upper Hanover from 1829 to
1840. According to his ledger, still extant,
he built 63 tall clocks in Lehigh County.
Here he uses "Saml. Krauss—Lehigh
County" and the German s is used.

L

Leibert, Henry   Norristown
                            Montgomery Co.
About 1849, Henry Leibert, a hatter by
trade, but also a clock- and watchmaker—
having learned these latter trades from his
father early in life—started a store in Norristown but drifted into the jewelry manufacturing business in partnership with
Samuel Brown. Leibert lost his life experi-
menting with gunpowder, as did his partner in the explosive-manufacturing enterprise, William Reiff.

Leigh, David   Pottstown
                            Montgomery Co.
Predecessor of John A. André in business
of clockmaking in Pottstown. André purchased Leigh's business.

Leinbach, Elias and John   Reamstown
                              Lancaster Co.
Period of activity, 1788–1810. Many of
their clocks were of the one-day type.

Lenhart, Godfrey   York Town
                                 York Co.
One of the original clockmakers in York,
residing at N. W. cor. George St. & Center
Square. Was making tall clocks in York
before the Revolution.
Godfrey Lenhart was the father of a noted
mathematician, William Lenhart (1787–
1840).

Leroy, Abraham   Lancaster
A Swiss who was making clocks in Lancaster at a very early period. From 1757 to
1765 he kept the court-house clock in
order. In 1750 Abraham Leroy returned to
Switzerland for a short period and left his
daughter—an expert clockmaker—in charge
of his business. This daughter married
Wilmer Atkinson.

Lewis, Curtis   Reading
Died 1847.
Possibly late 18th century but active in first
third of 19th century.

Lindsley, Timothy   Reading
Advertised in 1821. Died in 1825, aged 34
years.

Little, Archibald   Reading
Advertised in 1816 and 1819.

Lukens, Seneca   Horsham Meeting
                            Montgomery Co.
Died 1829.
The father of Isaiah Lukens, Seneca Lukens
was a self-taught clockmaker. He made a
clock for each of his four daughters. Clock
No. 41 made by Seneca Lukens is dated

1795. Isaiah Lukens was in business with his father for a while before going to Philadelphia.

M

Maus, John J.   Columbia
                                 Lancaster Co.
Was making clocks in Columbia about 1812.

Maus, William   Hilltown
                                 Bucks Co.
In business about 1810. Made several clocks.

Mears, William   Reading
Was working in Reading in 1785, and clock bearing his name with this date has been seen.

Mechlin, Jacob   Alsace Twp.
                                 Berks Co.
Mentioned as a clockmaker in Alsace Township manuscript dated Sept. 1759.

Mendenhall, Thomas   Lancaster
Clock, watch and instrument maker. Advertised in 1775.

Merimee, William   Brownsville
                                 Fayette Co.
Advertised in 1796 that he had returned from Kentucky and was ready to carry on his clock- and watchmaking business. (Brownsville, formerly known as Red Stone Old Fort, is in Redstone Township, Fayette County, on the Monongahela River, 35 miles south of Pittsburgh.)

Miksch, John M.   Bethlehem
Apprentice to Jedediah Weiss. Established in business for himself 1822. Died 1882. Succeeded by Edward F. Erwin.

Miley, Emanuel   Lebanon
This man's name appears upon many clocks originating in Lebanon. Very little is known about him other than that he was evidently a dealer who traded in many other articles in addition to clocks. His name appears also on old quilts still found in this region.

Miller, Rev. Harry Edwin   Lebanon
Born 1873, died 1947.
Up until 1942 this man had made 394 tall case clocks that were sent to all parts of the United States. He is unique in the annals of clockmakers in that he was a clergyman who also made clocks and in that he worked up until as late as 1942. His clocks appear much older than they actually are. He was born in Pine Grove, Schuylkill County, and spent his early days in the coal-mining area as a slate picker and breaker "man." At the age of 14 he removed to Lebanon and served his apprenticeship with the Lebanon Manufacturing Co. He was graduated from Lebanon Valley College in 1899 and from the Union Theological Seminary in 1903. He then became pastor of the Salem United Brethren Church in Lebanon. He was always interested in tall case clocks and spent much time repairing them. When he wanted one of these clocks for himself and could not procure an old one he built one. This started him upon clockmaking after the old school as an avocation. So well were his clocks made that he was soon deluged with orders.

Miller, Peter   Lynn Township
                                 Lehigh Co.
Born 1772, died 1855.
Probably made more clocks than any other maker in Lehigh County. Worked in brass and wood.

Montandon, Henry Lewis   Lancaster
Clockmaker who died in 1802. No clocks with his name on them have been found, but it is known that he made clocks.

Morris, Abel   Reading
Taxed as a clockmaker in Reading in 1774.

Morris, Benjamin   Hilltown
                                 Bucks Co.
Flourished about 1760. Made a great number of clocks.

Morris, Enos   Hilltown
                                 Bucks Co.
Son of Benjamin Morris. Learned trade with his father but studied law and was admitted to the bar in 1780.

Murphy, John   Allentown
                                 Lehigh Co.
Probably the earliest clockmaker in Lehigh County. Established as early as 1775

and lived there at least until 1790. Made a great number of clocks. (John Murphy clocks have "Northampton" as the place name, this being the early name of Allentown.)

Murphy, Thomas   Allentown
                                  Lehigh Co.
Was working in Allentown in 1830.

O

Oves, George   Lebanon
George Oves, clockmaker, married Elizabeth Buehler in Lebanon, Sept. 24, 1805.

Oyster, Daniel   Reading
Born 1766, died 1845.
Father died when he was one year old and he was raised by an uncle, Daniel Yoder. He was the youngest child of Samuel Oyster, blacksmith. In 1792 he married Catharine Rose, Reading, daughter of Erhard Rose. The family name is spelled variously Aister and Euster, but usually Oyster.

Q

Quest, Samuel   Maytown
                                  Lancaster Co.
Clockmaker in Maytown before 1813.

R

Rauch, James K.   Bethlehem
Apprentice to Jedediah Weiss, whose business he took over in 1865. Was still in business in 1892.

Reineman, Conrad   Chambersburg
                                  Franklin Co.
Conrad Reineman came to Chambersburg about 1834 and was a clockmaker and jeweler. He and his son Augustus V. Reineman were in business in Chambersburg for many years.

Rentzheimer, Henry   Salisbury Twp.
                                  Lehigh Co.
Clockmaker in Salisbury Township in 1785 and still lived there in 1788.

Roi, Henry   Hamburg
                                   Berks Co.
Sometimes signed himself "Henry King." Late 18th century and early 19th century.

Rose, Daniel   Reading
Born 1749, died 1827.
Son of Erhard and Eva Rose.
Served the county for many years in state legislature. Best of his clock work was done in latter part of the 18th century, after he had served as a lieutenant in the Revolution.

S

Scharf, John   Selingsgrove
                                   Snyder Co.
A Swiss clockmaker who came to Selingsgrove about 1836.

Scheid, Daniel
Spelled his name in many ways—Sheidt, Shaid, Shade.
Was active in business in 1854; his will was dated 1878. He was an excellent clockmaker but was in all sorts of financial difficulties during his lifetime.

Scott, Alexander   Chambersburg
                                   Franklin Co.
Alexander Scott, uncle of Thomas A. Scott, first president of the Pennsylvania Railroad, carried on a clockmaking and silversmithing business in Chambersburg from about 1800 until his death in about 1821. He manufactured a large number of eight-day tall clocks, which were celebrated for their correctness as timekeepers.

Shoemaker, David   Newtown
                                  Bucks Co.
Advertised as a clock- and watchmaker in 1817.

Shreiner, Martin   Lancaster
Born 1769, died 1866.
Started in business in 1790 and continued until 1830. Among the best and most extensive clockmakers of Lancaster County. Numbered all his clocks; the highest number known is 356. Also made fire engines, and in later life fire engines became the principal products of the Shreiners, father and sons.

Shreiner, Martin & Philip   Lancaster
Sons of Martin Shreiner.
Continued the business under the firm name of M. & P. Shreiner for six or seven years after 1830 when their father retired. Were forced out of the clockmaking business by the invasion of "Yankee" clocks.

Snyder, Peter, Jr.   Exeter Twp.
      Berks Co.
Mentioned as a clockmaker in 1779.

The Solliday family
This is undoubtedly the most numerous, if not the most remarkable, family of clockmakers not only in Pennsylvania, but in America. Several hundred clocks are accounted for by members of this family. The name seems to have originally been "Solede," but the now-accepted form "Solliday" will be used in this listing. No matter how exhaustive the research it seems that there will always appear yet another Solliday.

Frederick Solliday   Bedminster
      Bucks Co.
The family seems to have had its origin in America with Frederick Solliday, a clockmaker, who came from Basel, Switzerland, and settled in Bucks County. Frederick Solliday came in the ship *Queen of Denmark* and took the prescribed oath of allegiance Oct. 14, 1751.

Jacob Solliday   Bedminster
      Bucks Co.
The son of the original Frederick Solliday. A well-known clockmaker at the close of the Revolution; together with his son Peter Solliday pursued the trade as late as 1807. His clocks are marked "Jacobe Salede—Bucks County" and "Jacob Solliday—North Hampton."

Benjamin Solliday   Sellersville
      Bucks Co.
Brother of Jacob Solliday and son of the original Frederick Solliday.
Made clocks in Rockhill, near Sellersville.

Peter Solliday   Bedminster
      Bucks Co.
Born 1783, died 1859.
Son of Jacob Solliday.
Was in business with his father as late as 1807, and alone after that.

Samuel Solliday   Doylestown
      Bucks Co.
Son of Benjamin Solliday. Served his apprenticeship as clockmaker and set up in business in Doylestown.
Made tall clocks until 1833, when demand ceased. Moved to New Hope, where he became coal and lumber merchant in addition to clockmaking. Died 1885.

George Solliday   Montgomeryville
      Montgomery Co.
Son of Benjamin. Made clocks in Montgomeryville.

Daniel H. Solliday   Sumneytown
      Montgomery Co.
Daniel Hinckel Solliday, born in Sumneytown, where he worked as clockmaker until 1823. From 1824 to 1828 he was active in Evansburg, Lower Providence Township. Went to Philadelphia in 1829. (See Daniel H. Solliday in Philadelphia list.)

John N. Solliday   Tinicum
      Bucks Co.
John Nicholas Solliday lived at Tinicum near village of Point Pleasant. Was clockmaker and man of affairs as well as musician. In 1830 he made a fine musical clock. John N. Solliday advertised in Reading in 1816.
He died in 1881.

Spangler, Rudolph   York
Born 1738, died 1811.
Rudolph Spengler (also spelled Spangler) was a clockmaker and silversmith. His clocks are inscribed "Rudy Spengler, York Town." In the Revolution he was a captain of Sixth Company, York County Militia, which marched to "Eastern New Jersey" in 1776 to form the "Flying Camp."

Spangler, Jacob   York
Born 1767, died 1843.
The son of Rudolph Spangler. Was surveyor in early life and in 1818 was appointed surveyor general of Pennsylvania. He was known as General Jacob Spangler, since he was the commander of volunteer and militia regiments and was well versed in military tactics. There are six known clocks inscribed "Jacob Spangler, Yorktown."

Spellier, Louis H.   Doylestown
Bucks Co.
Born in Hanover, Germany, 1843, died in Philadelphia, 1891.
Learned clockmaking in Germany—came to Doylestown in 1869 and was clockmaker there until 1880, when he moved to Philadelphia. Studied electric clocks and time telegraphs, in which field he achieved distinction. In 1874 he exhibited clock with new escapement at The Franklin Institute, for which he received a silver medal, and he received another medal for the same clock at the Centennial in 1876. Developed a system of time telegraphy.

Starrett, James   East Nantmeal Twp.
Chester Co.
James Starrett was taxed as a clockmaker between 1796 and 1804 in East Nantmeal Township.

Stauffer, Samuel C.   Manheim
Lancaster Co.
Worked in the early 1800s and made very many fine clocks. At one time operated with Christian Eby under the firm name of Stauffer and Eby.

Stein, Daniel H.   Norristown
Montgomery Co.
The shop vacated by Isaac Custer was immediately taken over by William D. Rapp, of Philadelphia, in 1837 or 1838, and Rapp placed Daniel H. Stein in charge. Stein eventually took over the business and conducted it as his own for 40 years until his death in 1885.

Stein, Jacob   Allentown
Lehigh Co.
Born 1771, died 1842. Made many tall clocks.

Stein, George   Allentown
Lehigh Co.
Son of Jacob Stein. Some of the Stein clocks are marked "Jacob Stein & Co."

Stoner, Rudy   Lancaster
Rudy Stoner is the Anglicized form of Rudolph Steiner.
Born 1728, died 1769.
Clocks made by Rudy Stoner are rare; his business history is obscure, but evidently he was a man of substance.

Stoy, Gustavus   Lancaster
Clock- and watchmaker, as well as tavern keeper, in 1806.

T

Thomas, Joseph   Whitpain or
Norriton Twp.
Montgomery Co.
Learned clockmaking with Griffith in Philadelphia and was established in his own business in 1830. Was early president of Montgomery National Bank. Some of the Joseph Thomas clocks are marked "Penn Square."

Thomas, Isaac   Willis Town
Chester Co.
Born 1721, died 1802.
One of the best and most prolific clockmakers of Chester County.

Thomas, Mordecai   Willis Town
Chester Co.
Born 1767, died 1837.
Son of Isaac Thomas. Followed his father's clockmaking for a while, but had many other interests.

Thomson, James   Pittsburgh
Born 1790, died 1876.
Born in Franklin County near Chambersburg, James Thomson went west to Pittsburgh in 1812. From 1812 to 1825 he carried on a clock- and watchmaking business. Then entered into a partnership with Samuel Stackhouse for the building of steam engines under the name Stackhouse and Thomson. Firm was dissolved in 1839 or 1840, and then James Thomson became mayor of Pittsburgh. Later entered into partnership with Joseph Tomlinson building engines and freight cars. Still later was elected engineer of the Pittsburgh Gas Company.

Troth, Thomas   Pittsburgh
Clockmaker in 1815.

U

Urletig, Valentin   Reading
Arrived in Pennsylvania 1754, died 1783. Probably the first clockmaker in Reading. He was working in Reading as early as

1758. He made the clock for the first court house, erected in 1762. Urletig's clocks have brass faces with days of the month and phases of the moon.

W

Way, John   Waggon Town
                             Chester Co.
Born 1766.
Clockmaker and innkeeper. He left Waggon Town in 1798, and the history of his later life is not well known.

Weiss, John George   Bethlehem
Father of Jedediah Weiss. In 1795 John George Weiss took up clockmaking, merging into this occupation from nail, lock and gun smithing.

Weiss, Jedediah   Bethlehem
Born 1796.
Although still a minor at the death of his preceptor, John Samuel Krause, in 1815, he took over the business. He retired from business in 1865, when it was in turn taken over by his whilom apprentice James K. Rauch.

Weiss, Joseph   Allentown
                             Lehigh Co.
Born 1802, died 1863.
Made a large number of clocks.

Whitehead, John   Norristown
                             Montgomery Co.
John Whitehead advertised as successor to George Govett, when latter moved to Philadelphia in 1831. John Whitehead was in Philadelphia in 1848.

Wildbahn, Thomas   Reading
Born in Winchester, Va., 1763, died in Philadelphia 1805.
Many of Wildbahn's clocks have the rare sweep-second hands. Served as coroner and was charter member of Masonic lodge.

Wilson, William B.   Newtown
                             Bucks Co.
Advertised as clock- and watchmaker in 1826.

Wismer, Henry   Plumstead
                             Bucks Co.
Commenced work around the close of the 18th century and was busy until his death in Canada, near Lake Ontario, in 1828. Made many clocks and employed several workmen. Most clocks bear the name "Henry Wismer," with initials "B.C." for Bucks County, but do not bear township name.

Witman, Benjamin   Reading
Died 1857.
Late 18th century and early 19th. He advertised in 1796.

Witmer, Abel   Ephrata
                             Lancaster Co.
Born 1767, died 1821.
He was a member of the Cloister, where he lived and worked. He made a few clocks, all of the 24-hour type, but of exceptionally fine workmanship.

Y

Yeakel, Abraham   Perkasie
                             Bucks Co.
Came to Doylestown with Louis H. Spellier in 1869. Soon after moved to Perkasie, where he went into business for himself.

Yeakel, Solomon   Northampton City, now
                             Allentown
                             Lehigh Co.
Born 1773, died 1814.

Z

Zahm, G. W.   Lancaster
Retail jeweler, silversmith, and clockmaker in Lancaster from 1840 into the 1860s. His sons carried on the business at the same address, Penn Square, Lancaster, into the 1890s.

Zimmerman, Anthony   Reading
Died 1788.
Taxed as a clockmaker as early as 1768.

NAME INDEX

Note. For individual clock- and watchmakers see the Annotated Lists. Their names are not included in the index unless they appear in the text of the book. For clock- and watchmakers of Philadelphia, see list beginning on page 168. For those outside of Philadelphia, see list beginning on page 205.

This index has been divided into two parts: a name index and a subject index. The subject index begins on page 227.

Dates are given in this index whenever possible so that men, institutions, books, and events may be identified with their times. When birth and death dates are not available, other pertinent dates are given. No dates are given for men now living. Date and place of founding of each institution are given, as well as of companies. For books mentioned, author, date, and place of publication are given.

SUBJECT INDEX

In this index the dates of inventions and other milestones in the history of horology are given, wherever possible, so that subjects and events may be identified with their times.